(0)

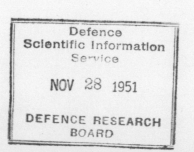

BIOCHEMISTRY
OF
GLUCURONIC ACID

BIOCHEMISTRY
OF
GLUCURONIC ACID

by

NEAL E. ARTZ, PH.D.

and

ELIZABETH M. OSMAN, PH.D.

Corn Products Refining Company, Argo, Illinois

1950

ACADEMIC PRESS INC., PUBLISHERS

NEW YORK

PREFACE

Since its discovery almost a century ago, no comprehensive study of the metabolic significance of glucuronic acid has been undertaken although many widely scattered observations bearing directly or indirectly on the subject have been recorded. Our purpose is to bring these observations together as a service and possibly as a stimulus to those investigators who, in light of the fact that glucuronic acid now is available in adequate quantities, may wish to undertake studies to establish the physiological role of this interesting carbohydrate oxidation product.

Many of the studies cited were not directed primarily to investigation of glucuronic acid and, in attempting to glean as much information as possible from these, the authors may inadvertently have attached more than due significance to some isolated observations. The role of glucuronic acid as a detoxifying agent has received much more attention than any other aspect of its metabolism. The meager and widely scattered information now available on most other functions sheds little light on this picture other than to suggest that systematic investigation of the significance of this compound should prove fruitful.

N.E.A. AND E.M.O.

Argo, Illinois
September, 1950

TABLE OF CONTENTS

Glucuronic acid may be considered as an oxidation product of D-glucose (I) although oxidation of the unmodified aldohexose does not ordinarily produce any detectable amount of this compound. The aldehyde group of glucose is much more susceptible to oxidation than any other position in the molecule and, consequently, the first product formed by most methods of oxidation is gluconic acid (II). Glucuronic acid (III or IIIa) represents glucose that has been oxidized at carbon 6 without carbon 1 having been attacked, a situation unlikely to occur during any simple oxidation of glucose.

| I | II | III | IIIa |

The name "glucuronic acid" should not be prefixed with D-, since in carbohydrate terminology assignment to the D- or L-series is made according to the configuration of the highest numbered asymmetric carbon atom in the chain, *i.e.*, farthest from the principal functional group; if the compound is named as an acid, this series-determining group, next to the aldehyde group, has the L-configuration. If, however, the compound were named as a sugar with the aldehyde group assuming the greater importance, the name would be "D-glucuronose."

Various terminologies have been employed to designate derivatives of glucuronic acid. Thus, the lactone (IV) of the acid commonly has been referred to as "glucurone." The term "glucuronolactone" appears more acceptable according to current carbohydrate nomenclature and therefore is used throughout this review. "Methyl glucuronide," "methyl glucuronic acid," and "methyl glucuronoside" all have been used to designate the compound (V). The latter term is preferable since the compound is a glycoside of glucuronic acid (D-glucuronose) and the currently accepted method of naming glucosides is to replace the ending "ose" of the parent sugar by "oside" and to prefix the name with that of the alkyl or aryl radical.

Glucuronic acid is a somewhat unstable compound and, so far as is known, does not exist in the free state in nature. As early as 1875, however, it was detected in the urine in a combined form after feeding certain "glucuronogenic" substances to animals. A large number of compounds has been found to provoke this response when ingested and, since most of these are toxic, the assumption naturally has arisen that conjugation with glucuronic acid represents a mechanism by which the organism rids itself of toxic substances.

IV*   V.*

In addition to being present in low concentrations in detoxication products in the urine and blood, glucuronic acid is present in mucopolysaccharides such as hyaluronic acid, heparin, chondroitinsulfuric acid and mucoitinsulfuric acid. Preparation of glucuronic acid from mucopolysaccharides is difficult; certain plant gums such as gum arabic form a better, although still unsatisfactory, source.

Most of the glucuronic acid that has been available for experimental purposes has been obtained by the biosynthetic route in which certain drugs are fed to animals, the urine collected, and the glucuronic acid conjugate is isolated and hydrolyzed to produce the free acid. Such a method necessarily is time-consuming and incapable of producing the compound in sufficient quantity to allow any extensive study of its metabolism. As a result, a large part of what is known of the physiology of glucuronic acid has been learned indirectly by observations made during study of the metabolism of other compounds that have been found to produce the "glucuronogenic response." For this reason the section on "Detoxication" makes up a large part of this review. The development of a satisfactory synthetic method for preparing glucuronic acid now makes this compound available in quan-

* IV has been shown to be the γ-lactone of the furanose (358, 398), whereas V probably has the pyranoid structure (146, 323).

tities sufficient to permit exhaustive study of its physiological significance, and solutions to some of the hitherto unsolved problems now should be attainable.

For example, most drugs are toxic to a certain extent and, since so many of these are eliminated from the body as conjugates with glucuronic acid, the question arises as to whether concurrent administration of certain drugs and glucuronic acid, either in chemical combination or separately, might diminish toxicity without appreciable loss of drug activity.

It has been demonstrated that certain residual groups representing normal metabolites are excreted as conjugates of glucuronic acid. Most metabolic products are toxic to the host organism if they accumulate, and the fact that some of these are excreted as this type of conjugate suggests a fundamental role for the mechanism. Abnormal, and frequently toxic, metabolites usually are formed when normal physiological processes are disturbed. Normal metabolites also may be produced in abnormally large quantities. Much of the damage resulting from infectious or other types of disease may result from accumulation of such materials. Since so great a variety of compounds are known to be eliminated from the animal body as conjugates of glucuronic acid, it seems possible that supplying additional amounts of this compound might assist in preventing accumulation of these harmful metabolites and thus alleviate severity of certain diseases or prevent harmful after-effects.

Presence of β-glucuronidase and hyaluronidase in tissues suggests a normal function; there is some evidence that activity of the former is confined primarily to cleaving glucuronic acid conjugates, the formation of which is effected under the influence of some other mechanism. Whether the only action of hyaluronidase is one of depolymerization has not been established. Both β-glucuronidase and hyaluronidase appear to be present in abnormal amounts under certain pathological conditions, but it is not clear whether this is a cause or a result of the pathology.

Some attempts have been made to determine the fate of ingested glucuronic acid, but results to date have not been conclusive. If further investigations demonstrate that ingested or injected glucuronic acid is available for conjugation or for the synthesis of mucopolysaccharides in the body, a thorough investigation of its possible therapeutic value would seem warranted.

This book reviews the published information on the biochemistry of glucuronic acid and may suggest fields for future investigation.

A. ANALYTICAL METHODS

No completely accurate and specific analytical method is available for the determination of glucuronic acid and development of such a method would be of tremendous value in studies of the chemistry and physiology of this compound. At the present time isolation of the crystalline product or one of its derivatives appears to be the only reliable method of demonstrating its presence. Table I lists the physical constants of pure compounds that have been isolated. Analytical methods now available are helpful, but interfering substances often lead to erroneous conclusions when these methods are used for analysis of biological fluids or synthetic reaction mixtures.

I. Naphthoresorcinol Method

The most widely used and perhaps the most accurate colorimetric method for the determination of glucuronic acid is the naphthoresorcinol test, although it leaves much to be desired. B. Tollens and Rorive (423) found that when solutions of different sugars were heated with a little naphthoresorcinol in the presence of an equal volume of concentrated hydrochloric acid, precipitates and characteristically colored solutions were formed. Glucuronic acid gave rise to a blue deposit. The precipitate was soluble in ether, giving a violet-blue solution, whereas precipitates obtained with sugars (pentoses, hexoses, etc.) were insoluble (422) and the reaction was used as a qualitative test for hexuronic acids. C. Tollens (424) attempted to adapt this qualitative test to the quantitative determination of glucuronic acid in urine.

Neuberg and coworkers (232, 301, 304, 307) studied the specificity of the test and the effect of various possibly interfering substances. They found that the presence of several compounds occurring in biological fluids greatly influences the intensity of the color developed. They further reported that the test was specific for sugar acids containing a carbonyl group, an assertion which is not substantiated by the statement of Huebner and Link (177) that D-arabo- and D-xylopenturonic acids differ from the hexuronic acids (D-glucuronic, etc.) in that they do not give the naphthoresorcinol and Bial reaction. Neuberg and Kobel (304) recommended the use of 50 per cent

5

sulfuric or 2 N hydrochloric in place of the concentrated hydrochloric acid, reporting that this modification eliminates the formation of resinous lumps during heating and causes the precipitate to form as a fine flocculent material which can be extracted easily by organic solvents such as ether, ethyl acetate, benzene, toluene, or chloroform. By using the diluted acid they claimed that sugars did not interfere even when present in a ratio of as

TABLE I

Compound	m.p.	$[\alpha]_D$	Reference
Glucuronic acid	165° (cor.)	$[\alpha]_D^{24}$ +16.05° (in H_2O, 3 min. after soln.)	(128)
		$[\alpha]_D^{24}$ +36° (after 3 hrs.)	
	156° (uncor.)		(435)
Glucuronolactone	167°–180°[a]		(68)
	176°–178°	$[\alpha]_D^{20}$ +20 (in H_2O)	(407)
	180° (cor., dec.)	$[\alpha]_D^{23}$ +18.55°	(128)
	175°		(300)
	175°–178° (dec.)	$[\alpha]_D^{20}$ +19.1°	(99)
Na salt · H_2O		$[\alpha]_D^{20}$ −0.56° (in H_2O) (initial)	(91)
		$[\alpha]_D^{20}$ +22.51° (after 1½ hrs.)	
K salt · 1½ H_2O		$[\alpha]_D^{21}$ +4.53° (in H_2O) (initial)	(91)
		$[\alpha]_D^{21}$ +20.02° (after 1½ hrs.)	
NH₄ salt		$[\alpha]_D^{20}$ −4.05° (in H_2O) (initial)	(91)
		$[\alpha]_D^{20}$ +23.17° (after 1½ hrs.)	
Ba salt		$[\alpha]_D^{20.5}$ +17.45° (in H_2O)	(91)
Brucine salt · H_2O	156°–157°	$[\alpha]_D^{20}$ −15.08° (in H_2O)	(91)
Semicarbazone of glucuronolactone	188°		(119)

[a] Melting points of highly purified glucuronolactone preparations have been found to vary between 167° and 172° C. when determined by the capillary tube method at heating times no greater than 5 min. Melts obtained by this method are clear and pale yellow in color. Coarsely crystalline preparations show higher and sharper melting points than finely powdered materials.

Erratic figures in the range of 175°–180° C. were obtained with a Dennis melting point bar calibrated with other compounds. Heating time on the bar affected results.

Discrepancy in melting points is perhaps due to incipient formation of volatile decomposition products, possibly water. Extent of decomposition and ease of escape of volatile products would be dependent on method used, time of heating, and particle size.

much as 30 parts to one part of the uronic acid or more, depending somewhat upon the sugar. However, they found the test unsuitable for quantitative determinations. Salt (369) applied the naphthoresorcinol reaction to urine from which interfering substances had been precipitated with lead acetate in slightly acid solution and found the color obtained was roughly proportional to the amount of glucuronate present. Florkin (108) obtained fairly good quantitative results with pure glucuronic acid and its salts when he purified the precipitate formed on condensation with naphthoresorcinol, then dissolved it in benzene and estimated the color in a photometer. Maughan, Evelyn and Browne (250) described a method which they found suitable for the quantitative estimation of glucuronic acid in the urine. They employed an aqueous solution of naphthoresorcinol which was stabilized in some manner by holding it at 38° for 24 hrs. and then kept in the dárk at 3°–5°. The color developed with this reagent was more intense than that obtained with an alcoholic solution of naphthoresorcinol. The colored product was extracted with peroxide-free ether and estimated in a colorimeter. Jarrige (188) stated that the effect of holding the solution at 38° is to allow equilibration between naphthoresorcinol and its oxidation product. Smith (404) also believed that the effect of this treatment is an oxidation of the naphthoresorcinol, and that the colored product actually is formed from this oxidation product rather than from naphthoresorcinol itself. The latter investigator prepares his reagent by aerating the solution with oxygen for an hour and removing the excess oxygen 24 hrs. later by bubbling nitrogen through the solution. A somewhat similar hypothesis receives support from the observation of Meyer, Bloch and Chaffee (265) that the color intensity of the complex of uronic acid and naphthoresorcinol was increased by potassium persulfate, although this suggests oxidation after condensation rather than before. A mechanism was suggested whereby two moles of naphthoresorcinol condense with one mole of uronic acid to give a xanthene derivative, the color of which is due to oxidation to a quinoid structure. Guerrero and Williams (135) also have proposed that the colored product is a xanthene or dinaphthylmethane derivative. These formulas do not, however, seem to account for the relative specificity as a test for uronic acids. If the uronic acid is connected with the naphthoresorcinol only through the aldehyde group, it seems strange that the remainder of the uronic acid molecule (a saturated side chain in these structures) should cause the pigment to differ

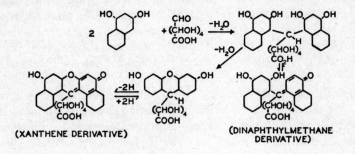

(XANTHENE DERIVATIVE)   (DINAPHTHYLMETHANE DERIVATIVE)

appreciably in color or even in solubility in organic solvents from products formed by aldoses or many of their derivatives. It also seems highly improbable that the uronic acid molecule remains unaltered except for the condensation during boiling with such high concentrations of hydrochloric acid.

Various other modifications of the Tollens procedure have been described. For example, Hanson, Mills, and Williams (145) suggest heating the reaction mixture for two hours and extracting the color with amyl alcohol. Since the mechanism of the reaction is not understood, it appears possible that some reported improvements in results may be caused by modifications other than those to which they are attributed.

Numerous procedures have been employed in applying the naphthoresorcinol method to biological fluids. Maughan, Evelyn and Browne (250), Hanson, Mills and Williams (145), Mozolowksi (286) and Deichmann (69) have described methods applicable to urine. Procedures based on the naphthoresorcinol reaction that have been used for the determination of glucuronic acid in blood include those of Mozolowksi (286), of Deichmann and Dierker (72), and of Ratish and Bullowa (356). When applied to polymeric substances such as the mucin of gastric juice, a preliminary hydrolysis is necessary, since all the uronic acid is not freed by the hydrochloric acid during the condensation reaction (397). As in all cases where colorimetric methods are applied to biological fluids, there is uncertainty as to whether some of the color produced may not result from an interfering substance. The accuracy claimed for these methods is seldom better than ±5 per cent, and it is doubtful whether even this degree of accuracy is obtained consistently.

II. Other Color Reactions

Several other color reactions can be produced by either a uronic acid or a pentose. Among these is the orcinol test which Bial (27) rendered more sensitive for pentoses by including a little ferric chloride in the reagent to retard color formation due to uronic acid. Scheff (375), however, reported a quantitative test for glucuronic acid based upon its reaction with Bial's reagent, but obviously this could not be used in the presence of pentoses. Goldschmiedt (132) used α-naphthol to produce a color which he claimed was not given by hexoses or pentoses. According to Thomas (421), β-naphthol may be used to distinguish between pentoses and hexuronic acid. When an aqueous solution of a pentose is added, without mixing, to a 0.3 per cent solution of β-naphthol in concentrated sulfuric acid, a blue ring appears at the interface, whereas glucuronic acid under the same conditions produces a crimson red ring.

When the Legal test (alkaline nitroprusside), ordinarily used for the detection of acetone, is applied to urine containing glucuronic acid conjugation products, a red to violet color is developed which is destroyed or changed to orange by addition of acetic acid (259). The red color developed by acetone under the same conditions is not destroyed by acidifying with acetic acid.

Dische (79) claims that a deep pink color, specific for glucuronic acid, results when mannose and glucuronic acid in concentrated sulfuric acid are allowed to react with a solution of thioglycolic acid. Since numerous other carbohydrates, including hexoses, pentoses and methylpentoses, form colors with thioglycolic acid, a blank reaction without the mannose must be carried out; the color is determined spectrophotometrically and the proper correction made. Galacturonic, pectic and alginic acids and Type I pneumococcus polysaccharide show a non-characteristic brown color with mannose and thioglycolic acid. Hexoses other than mannose form a pink color with glucuronic and thioglycolic acids, but the reaction is not specific for glucuronic acid as that with mannose is claimed to be. At best, this reaction appears to be complicated and it seems unlikely that it could be developed into a quantitative test of even as high a degree of accuracy as the naphthoresorcinol test. It may, however, prove useful in detecting glucuronic acid in the presence of galacturonic or other hexuronic acids.

When sugars are treated with concentrated sulfuric acid, they form products that react with carbazole to give a color (77, 156) which Egami (90) examined with a Pulfrich photometer. He found the maximum absorption band at filter S_{53}; in general this absorption band was most marked with the uronic acids. Dische (78) observed that different classes of sugars (*e.g.*, pentoses, hexoses, desoxypentoses) and even individual sugars of the same group (*e.g.*, mannose and glucose) show marked differences in rate of development of the color and in its absorption spectrum. By choosing appropriate conditions of acid concentration, temperature and time, he developed a quantitative test which is described as highly specific for hexuronic acids. It appears likely that the test can be developed for use with fluids of biological origin. This method is not reliable for conjugated glucuronic acid and polyuronides since some of these appear to give high and others low values for uronic acid, but it may be of use during isolation of the constituents of these compounds.

III. Decarboxylation Methods

Mann and B. Tollens (233) showed that glucuronolactone is quantitatively decarboxylated by the action of boiling hydrochloric acid, and Lefevre and Tollens (215) developed this reaction into a quantitative method for the estimation of glucuronic acid.   They boiled the substance to be analyzed with 12 per cent hydrochloric acid for $3\frac{1}{2}$ to 4 hrs. and measured the CO_2 evolved.   Other hexuronic acids undergo the same reaction.   The carbon dioxide is swept out of the reaction chamber with carbon dioxide-free gas, dried, purified and measured.   Various modifications have been described (50, 76).   Some carbohydrate materials which do not contain uronic acids also evolve carbon dioxide under this treatment, although at a slower rate than the uronic acids.   This fact led Norman (312) and also Whistler, Martin and Harris (437) to develop methods in which rate of evolution of carbon dioxide was determined, thus enabling them to detect the presence of uronic acids in substances such as cellulosic materials. The latter workers indicated that in acid concentrations above 12 per cent the rate of evolution of carbon dioxide by unoxidized glucose was too great to allow accurate analysis of substances with low uronic acid content. However, McCready, Swenson and Maclay (255) found that the use of 19 per cent hydrochloric acid speeds up the reaction appreciably and shortens the time of analysis.   The amount of carbon dioxide evolved by compounds other than uronic acids was no greater than during the longer period required at lower acid concentration, and in general the results appeared to be more accurate.

The most radical departure from the standard treatment with 12 per cent hydrochloric acid, however, was the method of Voss and Pfirschke (430); they used 20 M zinc chloride solution at its boiling point as the decarboxylating medium.

In addition to the small amount of interference afforded by ordinary sugars, a number of compounds that may be encountered in materials of biological or synthetic origin may cause pronounced interference in any carbon dioxide evolution method.   The extent of interference seems to vary in the hands of different workers.   Those substances reported to yield higher than 2 per cent by weight of carbon dioxide (theoretical for a hexuronic acid, 22.7 per cent) are listed in Table II.

Determination of the furfural produced during the decarboxylation reaction has been suggested a number of times as a method for estimating the amount of uronic acid present.   However, the yield of furfural is not quantitative and varies with reaction conditions.   Ehrlich and Schubert (92) found that 2.64 parts of galacturonic acid, upon distillation with hydrochloric acid and precipitation with phloroglucinol, give one part of furfural phloroglucide.   Myers and Baker (291) observed, however, that this factor is not constant but varies with the quantity of galacturonic acid.   Nevertheless, some workers have reported that the method gives sufficiently consistent results to be valuable in the determination of pectin (48). The procedure obviously is useless in the presence of pentoses or other compounds that yield furfural.

TABLE II

Material	CO_2 Evolved (% by wt.)	Reference
Potassium acid saccharate	4.50	(415)
D-Gluconic acid	8.16	(415)
D-Glucono-γ-lactone	7.72	(415)
Oxalic acid	4.97	(415)
Allantoin	5–22	(425)
Alloxan	8.9, 9.8	(425)
p-Aminobenzoic acid	3–4	(425)
Ascorbic acid	17.1, 18.7	(425)
Hypoxanthine	10.3	(425)
Pyruvic acid	4.7	(425)
	5.4	(313)
Urea	27.4, 25.6	(425)
2-Ketogalactonic acid	12.7	(226)

IV. Miscellaneous Methods

Optical rotation occasionally has been used as an indication of the presence of conjugated glucuronic acid in the urine. While the free acid is dextrorotatory, its conjugation products are generally levorotatory. If urine known to contain no albumin, β-hydroxybutryic acid, fructose or cystine is found to be levorotatory after it has been clarified with lead acetate in acid medium and then filtered, conjugated glucuronic acid is probably present.

Another indication of the presence of conjugated glucuronic acid in urine is an increase in reducing power after acidifying and boiling, indicating that conjugated glucuronic acid has been hydrolyzed.

Obviously both the above methods give only indications of the possible presence of glucuronic acid and should be confirmed by more accurate methods.

In study of the hydrolysis of glucuronosides, particularly by the enzyme β-glucuronidase, a method is needed to distinguish between the free and conjugated acid. Sometimes the free aglycon group can be determined. When glucuronic acid liberated is to be measured, reducing methods are employed. Some modifications have been made in the usual reducing tests and reducing values for the uronic acids have been calculated.

Among the reducing methods employed is the cerimetric method developed by Levvy (223).

Wise and McCammon (448) have published a table for determining sodium glucuronate and glucuronolactone using the usual gravimetric Munson-Walker method, and Kertesz (200) has tabulated copper equivalents to be used in the determination of glucuronic and galacturonic acids by Bertrand's method.

B. Occurrence

Glucuronic acid is not known to occur free in nature. In polymeric combination with other carbohydrate residues it is found in many plant gums and is also present in oxycellulose. It is present in conjugated form in low concentrations in normal blood and urine and the amounts are appreciably increased following administration of "glucuronogenic" substances. Certain mucopolysaccharides that are widely distributed throughout the body also contain glucuronic acid.

I. Blood and Urine

Small amounts of conjugated glucuronic acid occur in the normal urine, presumably combined with normal metabolites or toxic substances ingested in the diet. For example, Deichmann and Thomas (73) give the following lower and upper limits for normal excretion of glucuronic acid:

man (50 determinations), 65–306 mg. per day, average 164 mg.;
rabbit (131 determinations), 0–119 mg. per day, average 35 mg.;
rat (29 determinations), 3.4–8.7 mg. per day, average 8.4 mg.

Maughan, Evelyn and Browne (250) found that 375–456 mg. of conjugated glucuronic acid was eliminated by man in 24 hrs. and that the amount was increased to 1200–1400 mg. following administration of 3 g. of acetyl salicylic acid.

Although variation is high there is ample evidence that administration of substantial doses of compounds that conjugate with glucuronic acid does cause a marked increase in glucuronic acid output.

Deichmann and Dierker (72) found that the amount of glucuronic acid in serum or plasma varied between 0.4 and 2.5 mg. per 100 ml. in man, rabbits or rats. In rabbits or rats, this value was increased up to as high as 120 mg. per 100 ml. following administration of 2-methyl-2,4-pentandiol or cyclohexanone; the amount in the plasma paralleled that excreted in the urine.

Ratish and Bullowa (356) reported the average normal blood level of glucuronic acid in 110 patients as 7.5 mg. per 100 ml., with individual values ranging from 5–9 mg. They found a marked increase following adminis-

13

tration of sulfadiazine. These same authors found 0.5–2.6 mg. of glucuronic acid per 100 ml. in spinal fluid and 7.0–18.0 mg. per 100 ml. in pleural fluid.

Unreliability of analytical methods probably accounts for the rather wide differences in normal values that have been reported, and under these circumstances it can scarcely be assumed that normal levels have been established.

II. Mucopolysaccharides

The mucopolysaccharides are a group of naturally occurring polymers whose building units are carbohydrates or carbohydrate derivatives and which seem to occur closely associated with protein or peptide residues, perhaps as salts. Being products of cellular origin, it is not surprising that many different members of the class appear to contain the same building units. One of the most common of these units is glucuronic acid, which has been found to be a constituent of materials such as chondroitin sulfate, one of the major constituents of cartilage; heparin, a natural blood anticoagulant that occurs in the body; mucoitin sulfate from gastric mucin; numerous bacterial polysaccharides; hyaluronic acid sulfate of the cornea; and hyaluronic acid, a widely distributed polysaccharide of the body which has assumed considerable importance as a substrate for spreading or diffusing factors.

Although these compounds have received considerable study, precise knowledge of their structure awaits further investigation. Many of them, although important physiologically, are present in the body in very small amounts and are extremely difficult to separate in any degree of purity from natural hydrated protein complexes in which they occur.

Compounds of this type were first classified by Meyer (262, 263) who, however, included only hexosamine-containing compounds. Stacey (408, 409) proposed a classification which included many additional complex carbohydrates and some of the bacterial polysaccharides that are discussed later.

a. Hyaluronic Acid and Its Sulfate. Hyaluronic acid is a mucopolysaccharide found in animal tissues whose function appears to be that of binding water in interstitial spaces, holding cells together in a jellylike matrix and serving as a lubricant or shock-absorber in joints. An identical or closely related polysaccharide is found in some microorganisms. Both are hydrolyzed by the enzyme hyaluronidase, now considered identical with the "spreading factor."

Hyaluronic acid was first isolated from the vitreous humor of the eyes of cattle by Meyer and Palmer (269), and has since been isolated from human (271) and pig (110) umbilical cord, from bovine aqueous humor (270), from group A and C hemolytic streptococci (199, 388), from bovine and human synovial fluid (274), from a number of mesenchymal tumors such as fowl leucoses (193), from the pleural fluid in a case of malignant tumor of the pleura and peritoneum (267), from two cases of human synovioma (264), from Rous and Fuyinami tumors in chickens (329), from the skin of the pig (268) and rabbit (51) and from the sexual skin of monkeys (51). The compound also appears to be present in human skin (326, 431) and probably occurs in the nucleus pulposus of the intervertebral disc (264).

The polysaccharide occurs either free or in a saltlike protein complex from which it is difficult to separate. In combination with protein it forms a mucin "clot" when acidified to pH 4. Such a precipitation usually is the first step in isolation procedures, several of which have been described (137, 178, 253, 254, 271); products obtained vary in purity and viscosity. Hyaluronic acid appears to be composed of equimolar parts of glucuronic acid and N-acetyl-D-glucosamine, but the nature of the linkages between these units is unknown. Meyer (264) concluded from enzymatic data that the molecule probably contains few if any branched chains and that the basic unit is a disaccharide in which the aldehyde group of the acetylglucosamine moiety is free. The molecular weight appears to vary with the source, that of the product isolated from the navel cord being larger than that from bovine vitreous humor or synovial fluid. Blix and Snellman (30) estimated the molecular weights of products from these sources at 200,000 to 400,000 based on measurements of streaming double refraction. The apparent long-chain structures of this molecule and of chondroitin sulfate are of interest since, together with protein fibers, they may account for such properties as tensile strength and elasticity of connective tissues.

The presence of hyaluronic acid in the synovial fluid is of particular interest because of its possible involvement in rheumatoid conditions. The reported benefit of treating arthritic patients with salts of glucuronic acid (169, 328) may be connected with this polysaccharide in some obscure way. In the synovial fluid hyaluronic acid is combined with proteins, three of which, albumin, β- and γ-seroglobulin, have been found present (158). This protein-polysaccharide complex is characterized by a high viscosity which is believed due largely to the polysaccharide (367). When it was split by hyaluronidase obtained from any of its various sources (certain bacteria, testicle, sperm, skin, cornea, etc.), the viscosity dropped to almost that of water and progressively less cohesive materials could be precipitated by addition of acetic acid. This reduction in viscosity took place in a few minutes, although liberation of reducing substances by this enzyme occurred much more slowly (24 to 48 hrs.). Antiserums have reportedly been prepared that inhibit these changes. Traumatic inflammation of the joints was accompanied by a marked increase in the volume of synovial fluid (353). However, in most pathological conditions there usually was a decrease in the viscosity of the fluid which was believed to be caused by dilution with extracellular water or by the presence of a hyaluronic acid of lower molecular weight or by both.

Ragan and Meyer (354) have recently reported hyaluronic acid contents and relative viscosities of synovial fluids from the knee joints of 35 patients with rheumatoid arthritis and 11 patients without joint diseases. They found with very few exceptions that the apparent degree of polymerization of the hyaluronic acid was lower in the arthritic patients, although the total amount of the mucopolysaccharide present was greater. Hyaluronidase was not detected in joint fluid or in synovial or periarticular tissue and, in any event, its presence would not explain the increase in total hyaluronic acid. Therefore, it was concluded that the defect lies not in an enzymatic hydrolysis or nonspecific depolymerization but in abnormal synthesis of this polysaccharide, involving an increased production of incompletely polymerized hyaluronic acid.

Exposure to X-rays decreases the viscosity of human joint fluid without increasing the titratable acidity (indicating that the effect is not a result of oxidative degradation) or reducing its susceptibility to bull testis hyaluronidase (426). Because of the wide distribution of hyaluronic acid in the body, this effect was suggested as an important factor in the response of many tissues to X-ray therapy.

The site of origin of hyaluronic acid in the body is unknown. The presence of hyaluronate in ocular fluids and its absence from serum have been cited as evidence that it represents a secretion rather than a dialyzate (270). Meyer (264) has pointed out that the concept of synovial fluid as a dialyzate to which the "mucin" is added during passage through the connective tissue does not seem probable since, if such a mechanism exists, pleura and peritoneal fluid and lymph should likewise contain the "mucin," which has not been shown to be the case. The fact that a viscous fluid appears in cultures of synovial tissue (426) was cited by him as evidence that hyaluronate is a secretory product of some cells of the synovial lining. This seems to be borne out by the fact that hyaluronic acid has been isolated from a synovioma, not only at the site of the tumor but in metastases in the liver (264).

The abundant literature on the action of the enzyme or group of enzymes known as hyaluronidase, for which hyaluronic acid is the substrate, has been adequately discussed in a recent review article (264).

A polysaccharide composed of glucosamine, a hexuronic acid, acetic and sulfuric acid units in equimolar ratio was isolated from bovine cornea by Meyer and Chaffee (266). By rotation and by enzymatic analysis with hyaluronidase obtained from pneumococcus and from testis, they characterized the compound ás a sulfuric acid ester of hyaluronic acid.

b. Chondroitinsulfuric Acid. The intercellular substance of cartilage is composed almost exclusively of two components, collagen and chondroitinsulfuric acid. The latter is a mucopolysaccharide and appears to be composed of glucuronic acid, N-acetylchondrosamine and sulfuric acid. How these units are linked together has been the subject of several investigations and a number of structures have been proposed (42, 149, 221, 222, 276). Blix and Snellman (30) estimated the molecular weight at about 200,000, basing their value on measurements of streaming double refraction. As the result of electrophoretic studies on solutions of chondroitinsulfuric acid in phosphate buffer at a pH near neutrality, Wolfrom and Rice (451) reported that the material contains approximately equal amounts of stationary and moving components.

Polysaccharides composed of the same monomers as chondroitinsulfuric acid and apparently closely related to it have been isolated from umbilical cord (271) and from pig skin (268). The polysaccharides from both these sources, however, unlike the chondroitinsulfuric acid of cartilage, showed resistance to hydrolysis with a preparation of testicular hyaluronidase, and also had different optical rotations.

Mörner (284) believed that chondroitinsulfuric acid occurred in the tissue as a sodium or calcium salt. Meyer, Smyth and Palmer (272, 273), however, were of the opinion that it is present in cartilage in the form of a protein salt involving combination between the —COOH and —SO_3H groups of chondroitin sulfate and the —NH_2 groups of the protein. Partridge (325) takes the view that the actual situation lies somewhere between these two extremes, in that the strongly acid sulfate groups most probably are held in combination with some of the basic residues of the protein, the net charge of the complex being adjusted mainly by a competition between alkali metal ions and hydrogen ions for carboxylic acid residues in both protein and polysaccharide. The capacity for complex-formation exhibited by chondroitinsulfuric acid has led Partridge to visualize the structure of tissue as a network of collagen fibrils, in some places organized into parallel bundles to form microscopic fibers and in others relatively disorganized and heavily cross-linked by association with chondroitinsulfuric acid. He cited as supporting evidence the observations of Cohen (54). This investigator found that proteins of plant origin (molecular weight greater than 10^6) are precipitated by heparin, chondroitinsulfuric acid, and hyaluronic acid. The amount of carbohydrate in the precipitates was too small to be positively demonstrated by analysis. However, when the precipitate formed from tobacco mosaic virus and hyaluronic acid was incubated with hyaluronidase, the precipitate dissolved.

Certain pathological conditions are accompanied by a lowering of the amount of chondroitinsulfuric acid present in the cartilage. A. Meyer (260) has reported that in scurvy the cartilage is unable to fix the basic metachromatic colors as is normal cartilage. Since affinity for this metachromatic coloration depends on the content of chondroitinsulfuric acid, it was suggested that scurvy may involve impairment in ability to form this mucopolysaccharide, especially in view of the fact that fibers of the cartilage tissue are not formed. By analogy, and on the basis of clinical observations, Meyer concluded that the weakness of connective tissue in scurvy depends on inability to form chondroitinsulfuric acid.

Patellas that are affected to various degrees by chondromalacia contain less than the normal amount of chondroitinsulfuric acid (167) and the cartilage exhibits impaired elasticity with limited capacity for resisting loading whenever its chondroitinsulfuric acid is decreased. However, the chondroitinsulfuric acid content could be greatly reduced without causing disintegration of the tissue.

Goldberg (131) observed that one of the earlier changes in rheumatoid arthritis is a thinning of the articular cartilage as if it were being dissolved by an enzyme. There was also a rise in the pH of the cartilage, as evidenced by its staining reaction. It has been reported that beneficial effects are produced by administering salts of glucuronic acid to arthritic patients and was suggested that these effects may be related to a possibly decreased amount of chondroitinsulfuric acid present in such cases (169, 328).

c. *Mucoitinsulfuric Acid.* Glucuronic acid is the hexuronic acid constituent of the acid polysaccharide of the gastric mucosa of the pig (450). This polysaccharide also contains acetylglucosamine and ester sulfate (275) and is present in the gastric mucosa together with a neutral polysaccharide consisting of acetylglucosamine and galactose. From its electrophoretic behavior, mucoitinsulfuric acid has been reported to consist of a stationary component (40 per cent) and two moving components (41 per cent and 19 per cent) (451), but no further details have been published.

Mucin prepared from gastric mucosa was observed to have a pronounced effect in relieving patients suffering from peptic ulcers and this was first attributed to a combination of activities as a protective coating and as a buffering agent that prevented the corrosive action of acid in the stomach and intestine (11, 109). Dogs with biliary fistulae developed no duodenal ulcers when treated either with gastric mucin or with an alkaline powder, although normal incidence of ulcers in such animals is 40–60 per cent (202). However, animals receiving mucin showed better appetite, general condition, and maintenance of body weight than those receiving the alkaline powders.

Because of the chemical similarity of mucoitinsulfuric acid and chondroitinsulfuric acid, Crandall and Roberts (59) administered chondroitin to several patients suffering from peptic ulcers. Although the percentage of cases that showed definite improvement was lower (45 per cent) than reported for mucin treatment, the diets of these patients were in general substandard and the protective coating action to promote healing was absent. However, improvement was sufficient to suggest a common action of chondroitin and mucin. Glucuronic acid is common to both products and its administration in large doses was suggested, but apparently lack of a supply of the compound prevented experiments to determine the value of such treatment.

When chondroitin was added to the diet of dogs receiving cinchophen, the usual ulcerative process was much less acute and the time of survival was approximately doubled (118). Dogs receiving either mucin or chondroitin following an Eck fistula showed weight increases instead of the usual loss in weight (60). Administration of mucin following ligation of the common bile duct reduced the average loss of weight from 31 per cent to 7.3 per cent.

Indirect evidence that glucuronic acid may function in preventing gastric ulcers was reported by Manville (234). He depleted dogs of glucuronic acid by feeding menthol in increasing amounts until signs of intoxication appeared, showing that glucuronic acid could no longer be produced in sufficient quantity to meet the demand. Autopsy of these animals revealed ulcers in the stomach, pylorous, gall bladder, and small and large intestines. These ulcers bore a marked resemblance to those occurring in vitamin A deficiency; he suggested that the failure to produce a sufficient amount of glucuronic acid might be caused by a vitamin A deficiency. Miller *et al.* (277), on the basis of somewhat similar evidence, reached the conclusion that gastritis and duodenitis result from interference in normal metabolism of mucin of the mucosa incident to loss of glucuronic acid.

Because ulcer patients receiving chondroitin reported relief of chronic headaches, Crandall, Roberts and Snorf (61) were led to try chondroitinsulfuric acid in more than 150 cases of idiopathic headache (including migraine).   In 50 per cent of all instances practically complete relief was afforded and in another 20 per cent the severity or frequency of attacks was reduced by at least 50 per cent.   Again, glucuronic acid was suggested as the active factor.   These results led Crandall (57) to patent nontoxic magnesium, calcium and iron salts of chondroitin and of chondroitinsulfuric acid prepared from cartilage.   These preparations were claimed to be beneficial for the treatment of diseases such as migraine, urticarial eruptions, peptic ulcers, multiple sclerosis, various allergic phenomena, cachectic states associated with hepatic cirrhosis, obstructions in the biliary outflow, general nutritional disturbances and especially in nutrition in animals having Eck fistulae.

Although indications are that other factors also are involved, chondroitin has been reported to prevent gizzard erosion in chicks when added to a diet which otherwise causes these lesions (29, 151).   On the other hand Crandall and coworkers, using a variety of erosion-producing diets, failed to obtain unequivocal protective action from either commercial or purified chondroitinsulfuric acid (58).   However, they did find that the compound served as a growth factor for both the chick and rat (365).   This would be expected from the earlier work of Almquist *et al.* (4) who had shown that both glycine and chondroitin were active, and together could replace the "rice factor."   In addition, it was shown that glucuronic acid is the active component of chondroitin for the promotion of growth and that several substances related to it (sodium alginate, gum arabic, and certain pentoses) also are effective (3).

d. Heparin.   A very comprehensive review has been prepared by Jorpes (190) covering the chemistry and physiology of heparin and its application in medicine.   More than a brief résumé of the biochemistry of this mucopolysaccharide would be superfluous here, when so extensive a review of the literature is available.   Jorpes reports data indicating that the mortality from thromboembolism can be almost entirely eliminated, that prophylactic use of heparin prevents thrombosis to a very appreciable degree, and that proper and early use of heparin greatly reduces the incidence of indurations, ulcerations and disabilities that are late sequelae of thrombosis.

Heparin resembles chondroitinsulfuric acid and mucoitinsulfuric acid in that it is composed of glucuronic acid (449), a hexosamine (in this case glucosamine), and contains sulfate groups.   Most investigators also report the presence of acetyl groups as in the case of chondroitin- and mucoitinsulfuric acids, but Wolfrom's analyses (452) of heparin did not reveal their presence.   As with these related compounds, the structure of heparin has not been established, but considerable evidence is available to indicate that it consists of more than one component. Wolfrom and Rice (451) separated sodium heparinate by electrophoresis into two components, only one of which showed anticoagulant activity. Jensen and coworkers (189), however, reported activity in both the fractions they obtained by this method, although the component with the higher content of ester sulfate had the greater activity; they observed some indications of a third component. By frontal adsorption analyses they detected three components from one heparin preparation and four from another. Application of the Craig countercurrent distribution technique separated sodium heparinate into three fractions, all shown to contain carbohydrate, but only two of the fractions appeared to have anticoagulant activity (319).

One of the outstanding chemical characteristics of heparin is its high degree of substitution with sulfate groups. Anticoagulant activity appears to be directly related to the sulfur content of the material, being greatest in those preparations with the highest sulfur content (191). This relationship has been demonstrated further by the definite anticoagulant activity of such synthetic polysaccharide sulfates as cellulose trisulfuric acid and a chondroitin polysulfuric acid (195); activity of these compounds, however, is less than that of heparin and there was a marked difference in toxicity between the natural and synthetic anticoagulants.

The mast cells contain granules which are thought to consist of heparin (170). The location of these cells around the capillaries and small blood vessels makes it possible for them to void their granular contents into the perivascular tissue juices, or almost directly into the blood stream. In addition to acting as an anticoagulant, heparin from the mast cells may possibly also be a source of glucuronic or sulfuric acid for detoxication, as indicated by the depletion of the granular substance of dermal mast cells after applications of the toxic compounds phenol, naphthalene and benzene (412).

The exact mechanism of the anticoagulant activity of heparin is not clear. It appears to exert a multiplicity of actions possibly concerned with the physicochemical effect of the acidic polysaccharide on the different proteins involved.

e. Immunopolysaccharides. Formerly, it was believed that all antigenic substances were proteins. It is known now that some other substances, including certain bacterial polysaccharides, also are antigenic. The high degree of species specificity exhibited by the antibodies formed by proteins is not quite so apparent in the case of carbohydrates, possibly because of the smaller number of different monomeric units found in the carbohydrate series. Consequently, cross reactions with distantly related species are more common with carbohydrate antigens.

In his classic work on artificial antigens, Landsteiner showed that antibodies could be directed toward groups of known chemical constitution in an antigen, and could react with these groups by themselves. When this work was extended to the study of carbohydrates, Goebel and Avery (127) showed that antiserums could be formed against antigens containing sugar molecules linked to proteins (through the azophenyl group), and that glucose and galactose, which differ only in the steric configuration at the fourth carbon atom, could be clearly differentiated by means of such antiserums.

Goebel (121) later showed the antiserums to glucose- and to glucuronic acid-containing antigens were entirely distinct. Since these compounds have the same spatial configuration and differ only in the group on the sixth carbon atom, this differentiation illustrates the strong influence of acid groups on serological behavior. Introduction of an acetyl group in the same position diminished but did not abolish reactivity with the antiserum of the unchanged compound (129). The important role played by glucuronic acid in determining the serological specificity of certain bacterial polysaccharides was illustrated by the precipitin reaction of artificial glucuronic acid antigen with antipneumococcus horse serums types II, III and VIII (121). In this respect the synthetic glucuronic acid-protein antigen bears a striking immunological relationship to the specific bacterial polysaccharides. This relationship appeared to reside solely in the common glucuronic acid constituent known to be present in the specific capsular polysaccharides of these types of pneumococci. No such precipitin reaction occurred, however, with the antiserum of pneumococcus type I (121), in which the uronic acid constituent is galacturonic acid (154), or with antiserum produced by an artificial galacturonic acid-protein antigen (130).

An antiserum produced by an artificial antigen containing the azobenzyl glycoside of cellobiuronic acid (a dissacharide composed of one molecule of glucuronic acid and one of glucose, which is the structural unit of type III pneumococcal polysaccharide) gave a precipitin test with type III polysaccharide (123) when the latter was combined with a heterologous protein. This artificial antigen also reacted vigorously with antipneumococcus types II, III and VIII serums. The antiserum to this cellobiuronic acid-protein antigen conferred on mice a passive resistance to infection with virulent pneumococci of types II, III and VIII (124, 125). This artificial antigen also caused mice to acquire active resistance to infection with virulent type III organisms. These are apparently the first instances of the production of effective immunity to an actual disease by the injection of an artificial antigen containing a purely synthetic hapten.

Another type of serologically active carbohydrate that contains glucuronic acid, partially in the form of cellobiuronic acid groups, is that formed by oxidizing cotton selectively at carbon 6 of its glucose residues. Such an oxidized cellulose precipitated antipneumococcus types III and VIII horse serums, but failed to react with types I and II antiserums (152). A synthetic antigen also was prepared containing gentiobiuronic acid (VI) as a hapten (126); the latter differs from cellobiuronic acid in that glucose is attached through its carbon 6 group to the aldehyde group of the glucuronic acid moiety. This antigen formed precipitates with antiserums to gentiobiose and to cellobiuronic acid antigens, while its antiserum gave precipitin reactions with gentiobiose and cellobiuronic acid antigens. The gentiobiuronic acid antigen gave precipitin tests with antipneumococcal types III and VIII serums and reacted slightly with type II serum. Rabbit antiserum to this synthetic antigen did not agglutinate pneumococci types II or III, but protected mice against infection by type II pneumococcus. Since such immunization could also be obtained by glucuronic acid or cellobiuronic acid antigens, the *in vivo* protective action must be due to the glucuronic acid determinant group.

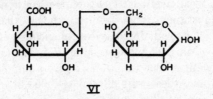

VI

The structure of pneumococcus type III polysaccharide probably is known more accurately than that of any of the other bacterial polysaccharides. As mentioned above, it is built up of aldobionic acid molecules composed of one molecule of glucuronic acid and one of glucose, united by a glucoside linkage involving the reducing group (aldehyde) of the glucuronic acid and carbon 4 of the glucose, giving cellobiuronic acid (VII) (174).

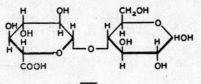

VII

The resulting aldobionic acid units are joined together by a glucoside linkage involving the reducing group of the glucose and the third carbon of the glucuronic acid residue (359). If the assumption that this linkage has the β-configuration is correct, and this seems probable, the constitution of the structural unit of this important capsular polysaccharide becomes completely known and, according to Reeves and Goebel (359), is:

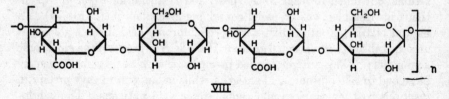

VIII

The minimum molecular weight of this capsular polysaccharide was first calculated to be 62,000 (153). Later workers (357), using ultracentrifuge and diffusion methods, reported a molecular weight of 141,000.

The polysaccharide of type VIII pneumococcus also contains cellobiuronic acid, but, in addition, contains glucose in some other form. Its minimum molecular weight has been calculated to be 140,000 (153). The polysaccharide of type II pneumococcus, with a reported molecular weight of 504,000 (357), is a weak acid that yields glucose on hydrolysis; the nature of its uronic acid constituent is not definitely known, although Goebel (121) stated on the basis of strongly indicative serological results that it probably is glucuronic acid. Marrack and Carpenter (236) found that an antiserum against type II pneumococcus would react with a number of natural vegetable gums, even when these were diluted 1:10,000 or more. They tested cherry gum, acacia gum, plum gum, apricot gum, gum ghatti, mesquite gum, gum tragacanth, and flax mucilage. With all except the last, precipitate formation was inhibited by salts of glucuronic acid and glucuronosides. These reactions not only illustrate the somewhat limited specificity of carbohydrates serologically, but again demonstrate the importance of glucuronic acid in these reactions. Boyd (36) has raised the interesting question of the possible effect on bacterial infection of ingesting similar carbohydrates in the diet. One might also consider the possible preparation of serums using synthetic antigens containing glucuronic acid, similar to the serum previously mentioned with which Goebel (125, 126) conferred on mice a passive immunity to infection with virulent pneumococci of types II, III and VIII; he used an antigen containing cellobiuronic acid to prepare the antiserum in this case.

The Friedlander bacillus also possesses a capsular polysaccharide which

seems to be responsible for type specificity.   The B type is similar immunologically to pneumococcus type II (12, 192).   The six strains which Julianelle classified as this type react as effectively with type II pneumococcus
antiserum as they do with their homologous antiserums.

Chemical determination of the structure of the capsular polysaccharide
of *Rhizobium radicicolum* (377) showed the presence of the cellobiuronic
acid unit, thus also relating this polysaccharide immunologically to the
specific polysaccharide of pneumococcus type III.   The structural unit is
thought to contain a second molecule of glucose.

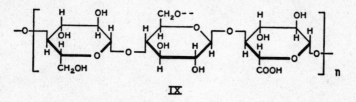

IX

Stacey (409) listed polysaccharides of two other bacteria, *Azotobacter* and
Cytophagae, as containing glucuronic acid.

C. Origin of Glucuronic Acid in the Body

Various workers during the past 70 years have proposed mechanisms for the formation of glucuronic acid in the body. Some of these have since been proved invalid and existing data are conflicting. Much additional work is required before the site and mode of formation of this important compound are known with certainty.

The earliest and simplest hypothesis was that glucuronic acid is produced in the body by direct oxidation of D-glucose. Schmiedeberg and Meyer (381), after deciding that glucuronic acid was a derivative of glucose, concluded that it probably was a normal metabolic intermediate that escaped further oxidation by combining with compounds such as camphor to form a derivative which was excreted. Sundvik (411), and later Fischer and Piloty (99) postulated the initial formation of a glucoside by such compounds as camphor, phenol, etc. With the easily oxidized aldehyde group of the glucose thus protected, they believed that oxidation then took place at the primary alcohol group with the formation of a conjugated glucuronic acid.

Some experiments were reported which appeared to support this theory. After subcutaneous administration of coniferin (coniferyl glucoside), syringin (methoxyconiferyl glucoside) or bornyl glucoside, conjugated glucuronic acids were excreted (163, 165); in the case of coniferin, the conjugate contained the oxidation product of coniferyl alcohol rather than the alcohol itself. Glucosides of several other terpene alcohols produced similar results (143). A more likely explanation has been suggested for these observations (447). Instead of the glucoside being oxidized directly *in vivo* to the glucuronoside it may first be hydrolyzed to give an aglucone which then combines with preformed glucuronic acid or its precursors. Data supporting this latter explanation are as follow:

(a) When the glucoside phloridzin was administered to animals, it was excreted as phloridzin glucuronoside (382) in which the original glucose molecule remained unchanged and glucuronic acid was attached to one of the originally free hydroxyl groups of phloridzin. Therefore, the glucuronic acid was not derived from the glucose originally present in phloridzin.

27

(b) Neither bornyl β-glucoside nor phenyl β-glucoside gave rise to conjugated glucuronic acids when added to the perfusing blood in a
pump-lung-liver-kidney preparation which could synthesize conjugated glucuronic acid from free borneol or phenol (155). It was
found that guinea pig liver slices that could produce conjugated
glucuronic acid in the presence of suitable concentrations of borneol
did not produce the conjugation product from bornyl β-glucoside
(224).

(c) When phenyl β-glucoside was injected into or fed to rabbits, the excretion of ethereal sulfate was increased to the same extent as when
an equivalent dose of phenol was administered, thus indicating the
in vivo hydrolysis of phenyl glucoside to phenol (335, 336).

(d) Although administered potassium phenylsulfate and injected phenyl
glucuronoside are excreted almost quantitatively unchanged by the
rabbit, orally administered phenyl glucuronoside causes a considerable rise in ethereal sulfate excretion and small amounts of oxidation
products of phenol are formed (116, 292).   This evidence suggests
that phenyl glucuronoside is at least partially hydrolyzed in the
intestine yielding free phenol, which then is excreted in the usual
way.

Another simple explanation for the origin of glucuronic acid that has
been advanced but which does not appear in keeping with the majority of
experimental evidence is that it is derived from ingested materials containing preformed glucuronic acid.   One hypothesis is that it is derived from
the digestion of mucin or other glucuronic acid-containing products and is
stored in the body, probably in the form of a deposit protein, as a readily
available source for conjugation with toxic substances (277, 278).   Such
glucuronic acid-containing materials are ingested in connective tissue and
in greens.   Although suggestions that such preformed glucuronic acid cannot be utilized are open to some question, there seems little doubt that other
precursors are responsible for the greater part of the glucuronic acid formed
in the body.   Baier *et al.* (14) suggested that hexuronic acids in the animal
body do not consist entirely of glucuronic acid but that galacturonic acid
derived from ingested pectic materials also is present.   While it is true
that the ordinary tests used to detect glucuronic acid do not distinguish
between these two compounds and some galacturonic acid might be present, it seems unlikely that the latter occurs to the extent they suggested.
In all cases in which the uronic acid portion of excreted uronosides has been
identified, it has proved to be glucuronic acid.   In all cases where the

hexuronic acid of mucopolysaccharides occurring in the body has been identified, it too has proved to be glucuronic acid. Furthermore, although these investigators conclude that the uronic acid in the liver of adult rabbits is probably galacturonic acid because the animal is herbivorous and ingests a diet containing pectic substances rather than mucin, Williams (443) reports the isolation of 40 g. of glucuronolactone for each 100 g. of menthol fed to rabbits, indicating that the uronic acid excreted must be largely glucuronic. It also has been reported by Werch and Ivy (436) that less than 10 per cent, if any, of the galacturonic acid introduced as an isosmotic and isotonic solution is absorbed from the canine or human intestine.

There seems little doubt that liver glycogen is in some way involved in the formation of glucuronic acid in the animal body. Direct evidence is contained in the experiments of Dziewiatkowski and Lewis (89). They found that 4 hours after oral administration of sodium *tert*-butylacetate or *l*-menthol to well-fed young rats the glycogen content of the liver was greatly depleted in comparison to that of control animals receiving water alone or sodium *n*-butyrate (which does not form a conjugate of glucuronic acid). Both sodium *tert*-butylacetate and *l*-menthol increased the excretion of glucuronic acid and it therefore appeared that liver glycogen is a precursor of glucuronic acid.

Further evidence that glycogen is a precursor of glucuronic acid may lie in the experiments of Schmid (378) on hibernating frogs. The well-fed frog is able to produce conjugated glucuronic acid in response to various toxic substances. Whereas the liver of a well-fed frog contains 60–200 mg. of glycogen, this is decreased to about 0.25 mg. during the period of hibernation. Schmid kept three groups of frogs in jars containing 50 ml. of water. The first group was well fed, the second starved, and the third was starved but the water in this jar contained glucose or glycogen. Each animal then received 15–20 mg. of menthol orally. In the first and third groups there resulted no sign of intoxication and the surrounding water eventually gave a positive Tollens naphthoresorcinol test for glucuronic acid. The second group succumbed to narcosis within 1 hour after administration of the menthol and died in one to two days; the surrounding water gave a negative naphthoresorcinol test. These experiments indicate that preformed carbohydrates, such as glucose or glycogen, are necessary for the formation of conjugated glucuronic acid in the frog.

Results with other starving animals are confusing and contradictory. Concerning such experiments Quick (342) stated that these experiments proved nothing one way or another, in view of current knowledge concerning the tenacity with which the body conserves its store of glycogen and its

power to convert protein to glucose and glycogen.   Thierfelder (417) gave
6 g. of chloral hydrate to a dog that had been starved for 17 days and was
assumed to be glycogen-free.   It excreted 5.72 g. of urochloralic acid and
Thierfelder therefore suggested that the protein of the body was the probable source of the glucuronic acid in this compound.   Mayer (251), on the
other hand, found that the ability of starving rabbits to synthesize conjugated glucuronic acid in response to administered camphor was diminished,
but that normal conjugation could be restored by administration of glucose,
and he claimed that glucuronic acid originated from glucose in the body.
These experiments of Mayer could not be duplicated by Fenyvessy (98),
who found that rabbits fasted for 12 days showed neither a decrease in
glucuronic acid output in response to phenol, camphor or chloral hydrate
nor an increase when these substances were administered with glucose.
Experiments of Mandel and Jackson (231) on starving dogs seemed to confirm Thierfelder's suggestion.   They fed camphor to starving dogs and determined the nitrogen output under various conditions.   They reported
that on feeding large amounts of glucose to the camphor-treated dogs there
was a large diminution in both the nitrogen and the camphoglycuronic acid
output, whereas on feeding chopped meat there was a corresponding increase in both.   Constant elimination of camphoglycuronic acid occurred
as long as meat and camphor were fed.   While none of these experiments
on fasting animals is conclusive, the results strongly suggest both carbohydrate and protein as precursors of glucuronic acid.

Loewi (225), experimenting with phloridzinized animals, concluded that
glucose and glucuronic acid have different precursors and that glucuronic
acid is not derived from glucose.   He assumed that if glucose and glucuronic acid have the same precursor, administration of a glucuronogenic
drug to a diabetic animal would cause a decrease in glucose excretion corresponding to the glucuronic acid produced.   However, after giving camphor
to meat-fed phloridzinized dogs, he found neither a significant decrease in
sugar excretion nor a greater than expected drop in nitrogen excretion; the
glucose-nitrogen ratio was raised rather than diminished.   His method for
the determination of conjugated glucuronic acid was questionable since he
relied on polarimetry, and the urine in these experiments probably would
contain a variety of optically active substances.

Quick (342, 343), experimenting along the same line with depancreatized
dogs, used sodium benzoate and borneol as glucuronogenic drugs.   He
measured the $\dfrac{\text{glucose}}{\text{nitrogen}}$ ratio and, after administering the drug, the

$$\frac{\text{glucose} + \text{glucuronic acid}}{\text{nitrogen}}$$ ratio. If glucose and glucuronic acid have the same precursors the numerical values of these ratios in the depancreatized dog should be the same. This was found to be approximately true. Quick concluded that glucose and glucuronic acid produced in the fasting diabetic dog have the same precursor, probably lactic acid, and that when there is a demand on the organism for glucuronic acid, it is produced at the expense of potential glucose. Since the production of glucuronic acid was not accompanied by an increase of urinary nitrogen when sufficient carbohydrate was provided, it appeared that the organism can produce glucuronic acid from this source. After a period of fasting, simultaneous administration of glucose and sodium benzoate did not prevent increased nitrogen catabolism, a fact which Quick took to indicate that the precursor of glucuronic acid probably is derived more readily from glycogen and glycogenic amino acids than from glucose. In later experiments, however, Quick (352) found that lactic acid, glycolic acid, and acetoacetic acid all decreased the output of glucuronic acid by dogs receiving benzoic acid, and he concluded that these compounds were not precursors of glucuronic acid. On the other hand, he found that administration of insulin with sucrose strikingly increased the excretion of glucuronic acid. Vescia (428) reported that insulin treatment of diabetics receiving menthol caused increased elimination of glucuronic acid, but that the blood sugar did not diminish. He was led to believe that hepatic glycogen was the source of glucuronic acid.

Quick's earlier suggestion that glucuronic acid may be derived from a simple compound such as lactic acid has received support from the tissue slice experiments of Lipschitz and Bueding (224). They found that guinea pig-liver slices poor in carbohydrate, i.e., from fasted animals, produced very little glucuronic acid in the presence of borneol but that synthesis was greatly stimulated by the presence of certain three-carbon compounds such as dihydroxyacetone and salts of lactic and pyruvic acids. Other important carbohydrate metabolites such as glyceraldehyde, phosphoglycerate, methylglyoxal, α-glycerophosphate and hexose diphosphate were ineffective and glycogen, glucose, glucosamine and fructose appeared to have only slight effect. These workers also concluded from rather unconvincing data that glucuronic acid itself cannot be utilized for conjugation by the liver slice. They decided therefore that glucuronic acid for conjugation purposes was derived neither from preformed glucuronic acid nor directly from glucose, glycogen or protein, but from a simple three-carbon precursor (or precursors); it could however be derived indirectly from glucose, glycogen or the glucogenic portion of proteins, insofar as they are converted during their metabolism into the simple precursor (or precursors) of glucuronic acid.

Crépy (62) found that addition of glucose or glucuronic acid to estrogen-liver slice preparations caused no increase in conjugation, but obtained the same results with lactic and pyruvic acids; the inference was drawn that tissue glycogen may be the source of glucuronic acid for conjugation.

It has been quite generally accepted that the liver is the main site of formation of urinary glucuronosides. The basis for this supposition lies in experiments such as those of Nishimura (311), who found that following complete removal of the liver of a dog the glucuronic acid excretion was greatly decreased and that injection of camphor failed to cause an increase. Failure of patients with liver damage to produce normal quantities of glucuronic acid in response to glucuronogenic substances has led to the suggestion that this abnormality be used as a possible basis for a test for liver function (32, 34, 289, 293, 322, 374, 405, 406).

Lipschitz and Bueding (224) showed that kidney slices are capable of bringing about the formation of small amounts of glucuronic acid conjugates. However, the relative size of the liver in comparison with most of the other organs makes it of prime importance if the concentration of the enzyme system responsible for glucuronic acid conjugation is similar.

The existence in animal tissue of an enzyme which hydrolyzes β-glucuronosides was reported by Sera (391) in 1915. Masamune (247) in 1934 described the preparation of extracts containing this enzyme from ox kidney, and in the same year Oshima (320) reported the glucuronidase content of various tissues of the dog and the ox; liver, spleen, kidney, ovary, testes and thymus were particularly good sources. More recently the glucuronidase activity of many tissues, both normal and pathological, has been studied and various improved methods of purifying the enzyme have been reported. Most investigations have dealt with the active principle as a single enzyme, but Mills (279), Mills and Paul (280) and Kerr, Campbell and Levvy (201) detected and were able to separate two forms of glucuronidase in several tissues, including spleen, liver, kidney, uterus, thymus and blood plasma. The latter investigators found only one form in the uterus of the mouse. The two enzymes differed in that one had a pH optimum at 4.5, the other at 5.2.

Becker and Friedenwald (20), measuring glucuronidase activity in the hydrolysis of phenolphthalein glucuronoside, found its action was almost completely inhibited by ascorbic acid and to a lesser extent by heparin. The hyaluronidase in testes preparations had an accelerating effect on glucuronidase, presumably by removing an inhibitor.   Glucuronidase is also inhibited by saccharic acid (196) but closely related compounds, including glucuronic acid, were less effective.   Saccharic acid had no marked effect on synthesis of o-aminophenyl glucuronoside by mouse liver slices. β-Glucuronidase did not promote conjugation of o-aminophenol with glucuronic acid.

Evidence that β-glucuronidase is distinct from the enzyme system responsible for glucuronic acid conjugation was presented by Karunairatnam, Kerr and Levvy (197).   Whereas conjugation occurred only in liver and kidney, glucuronidase was present in practically all tissues studied.   They found that the glucuronoside-synthesizing power of the liver of young mice, which was essentially zero at birth, increased rapidly to a maximum at 4 to 5 weeks.   On the other hand, glucuronidase activity, which was high during the initial period of rapid growth, decreased to a minimum at about the same time glucuronoside-synthesizing power reached a maximum.

This later work indicates the need for a re-interpretation of some of the data reported by Fishman.   He assumed (100) that the occurrence of the enzyme β-glucuronidase in tissues presupposed a reversible reaction: β-glucuronoside $\rightleftharpoons$ aglucone $+$ glucuronic acid.   Houet, Duchateau and Florkin (175) reported a slight synthesis of conjugated glucuronic acid from glucuronic acid and borneol by a β-glucuronidase preparation at pH 4.5. Assuming such a synthetic role for glucuronidase, Fishman (100) reasoned that the glucuronidase content of tissues might be increased by administration of glucuronogenic substances in the same way that certain enzymes are increased in some microorganisms by adding their substrates to the culture media.   He observed increases in the β-glucuronidase activity of liver, kidney and spleen of dogs and mice that had been fed borneol and menthol, respectively.   No increase in β-glucuronidase activity of the sex organs was noted, which was taken as an indication that in these organs the enzyme may not be concerned primarily in the general detoxication processes of the body but in the metabolism or transport of the sex hormones.   However, following the administration of estrogens, Fishman (101) found an increase in β-glucuronidase activity only in the uterus and possibly the vagina, and he took these results to indicate that conjugation of these substances probably occurs there, rather than in the liver.   On the other hand, Crépy (62) observed that estrogens were conjugated on liver slices.

The work of De Meio and Arnolt (75) suggests that phenol may combine directly with glucuronic acid in liver slices.   Conjugation of phenol in tissue slices was inhibited by 0.002 molar iodoacetate; on addition of glucuronate the conjugation was reestablished, but lactate was ineffective.   The inhibitory effect of iodoacetate thus appeared to effect the formation of glucuronic acid and not its conjugation with phenol.

It is reported that administered glucuronic acid is oxidized only with difficulty in the dog and the rabbit (28) and is largely excreted unchanged. Some may, however, be transformed into 2,5-furan-dicarboxylic acid in man, since Flaschenträger, Cagianut and Meier (105) found that the normal urinary output of this acid was increased 5–15 times by the administration of 5 g. of glucuronolactone or galacturonic acid. Ingestion of glucuronic acid by pentosurics caused greatly increased elimination of pentose in the urine, but no pentose was found after glucuronic acid was fed to normal persons (96).

Sylvén and Larsson (412) observed that single applications of benzene, phenol and naphthalene to mouse skin cause an early depletion of the granular substance of dermal mast cells. This granular substance is thought to be largely heparin, a mucopolysaccharide of which glucuronic and sulfuric acids are constituents. This could possibly suggest mobilization of preformed glucuronic acid from mucopolysaccharides of the organism.

From the above data it is obvious that the exact nature of the precursor (or precursors) of glucuronic acid and the mechanisms of synthesis of conjugated glucuronic acid remain to be established and that much more work on this subject is required.

D. Detoxication

The term "detoxication," as generally accepted today by biochemists, is somewhat of a misnomer, since it has become customary to describe as a "detoxication reaction" any chemical change occurring in the body which brings about the conversion of a foreign compound of known structure to a derivative which is excreted in the urine. These changes usually involve oxidation, reduction or various conjugations, oxidation or reduction often preparing the foreign molecule for a subsequent conjugation. Williams (447) lists nine such "conjugations." They are:

1. glucuronic acid conjugation
2. ethereal sulfate conjugation
3. glycine conjugation or hippuric acid synthesis
4. cysteine conjugation or mercapturic acid synthesis
5. ornithine conjugation or ornithuric acid synthesis
6. glutamine conjugation
7. acetylation
8. methylation
9. thiocyanate detoxication

Not all of these mechanisms are possible for all animal species and, more important, not all of them actually result in reduced toxicity when they occur. Glucuronic acid conjugation is by far the most common of these syntheses. It has been found to occur in all species studied, and appears to result in a reduction in toxicity and greatly increased solubility at physiological pH levels.

Perhaps the earliest indication of glucuronic acid conjugation was the observation by Schmid (379) in 1855 that euxanthic acid, on acid hydrolysis, yielded a copper-reducing substance. This was confirmed by Baeyer (13) in 1870. On the basis of the equation for formation of euxanthone from euxanthic acid, Baeyer stated that the reducing substance, which he termed "a kind of saccharic acid," should have the formula $C_6H_{10}O_7$, which now is known to be correct for glucuronic acid. Mering and Musculus (258) in 1875 observed that, following ingestion of chloral hydrate, man excreted in the urine a compound which is strongly acidic, copper-reducing and levorotatory. This compound was isolated in crys-

35

talline form and named urochloralic acid. Baumann (16) found in 1877 that animals receiving indole excrete, in addition to indoxylsulfuric acid, a compound containing indole combined with an organic radical, now known to be glucuronic acid.

The first clear evidence of the nature of glucuronic acid was obtained by Jaffe (182, 183) during an investigation of the fate of p-nitrotoluene and o-nitrotoluene in the dog. He found that whereas p-nitrotoluene was chiefly oxidized to p-nitrobenzoic acid and excreted as p-nitrohippuric acid, only about 10 per cent of the *ortho* compound was oxidized to the corresponding acid. The main product, corresponding to 25 per cent of the o-nitrotoluene fed, was a substance which he called "Uronitrotoluolsaure," $C_{13}H_{15}NO_9$. Its properties suggested that it might be a glucoside, *i.e.*, a compound of o-nitrobenzoic acid and glucose. Hydrolysis with dilute sulfuric acid, however, produced the then unknown o-nitrobenzyl alcohol and a residue which was levorotatory, reducing, acidic and nonfermentable by yeast. Jaffe represented the hydrolysis by the following equation:

$$C_{13}H_{15}NO_9 + H_2O = C_7H_7NO_3 + C_6H_{10}O_7$$

The syrupy "hypothetical acid," $C_6H_{10}O_7$, he considered to be carbohydrate in nature, an aldehyde-acid produced by oxidation of the primary alcohol group of the sugar to a carboxyl group. He further suggested that this acid was a probable component of the urochloralic acid of Mering and Musculus, a fact later confirmed by Mering (256).

In 1879 Schmiedeberg and Meyer (381) isolated glucuronic acid as the lactone from the camphoglycuronic acids excreted by dogs that had been fed camphor, and suggested that it was identical with Jaffe's "hypothetical acid." They proposed the name "Glycuronsaure" and deduced the structure to be $(CHOH)_4 \begin{cases} CHO \\ COOH \end{cases}$. Unlike Jaffe's product, their acid was dextrorotatory, but they explained this discrepancy by the assumption that Jaffe's acid probably was contaminated with the strongly levorotatory "Uronitrotoluolsaure." They believed glucuronic acid probably represented an intermediate in the metabolism of sugar protected from further oxidation by conjugation.

It is now recognized that conjugated glucuronic acid, in small amounts, is a normal constituent of the urine, presumably combined with normal metabolites or toxic substances ingested in the diet. Although normal variation is high, there is ample evidence that administration of substantial doses of compounds which conjugate with glucuronic acid does cause a marked increase in glucuronic acid output. However, because of the unreliability of analytical methods for determination of glucuronic acid, isolation of the glucuronoside appears to be the only completely reliable method for determining its presence.

I. Aliphatic Compounds

Unsubstituted aliphatic primary alcohols, aldehydes and acids are oxidized relatively completely in the body and only small amounts of their metabolites find their way into the urine. Branching and substitution tend to inhibit oxidation and to result in metabolites which are excreted in conjugation with glucuronic acid and can be isolated. Many investigations in the field of aliphatic compounds were reported before quantitative methods for determining glucuronic acid had been developed and, in some cases, before a qualitative method with any degree of specificity was known. Therefore, except in cases where crystalline products were isolated, much of the work needs confirmation.

ALIPHATIC ALCOHOLS

Primary Alcohols. Neubauer (299), using tests of doubtful reliability (orcinol test, reducing value and polarimetry), reported that ethyl, *n*-propyl, *n*-butyl, isobutyl, *n*-octyl and isopentyl alcohols cause increased excretion of glucuronic acid in both the rabbit and the dog, the response being more pronounced in the rabbit. On the contrary, methyl alcohol apparently did not increase glucuronic acid production.

Tribromoethyl alcohol, "avertin," is excreted as tribromoethyl glucuronoside (m.p. 145.5°; $[\alpha]_D$ −79.09°) which has been isolated from the urine of rabbits after ingestion of the alcohol (95). Trichloroethyl alcohol appears to be excreted partly unchanged and partly as trichloroethyl glucuronoside (urochloralic acid) (216).

Secondary Alcohols. In addition to reporting that primary alcohols cause an increased excretion of glucuronic acid, Neubauer (299) claimed a similar effect after administration of isopropyl, *sec*-butyl and *sec*-octyl alcohols. In contradiction, Neymark (310) has reported the quantitative transformation of isopropyl alcohol to acetone in the dog. Neuberg and Gottschalk (303) claimed that in rabbits acetoin (3-hydroxy-2-butanone) forms a glucuronoside, either from acetoin itself or from its metabolite, 2,3-butylene glycol.

Tertiary Alcohols. Tertiary butyl alcohol, when fed to rabbits, is excreted as *tert*-butyl glucuronoside, the potassium salt of which was levorotatory (419). This conjugation apparently does not occur in dogs.

Tertiary pentyl alcohol, when fed to rabbits, also forms with glucuronic acid a conjugate which has been isolated as a potassium salt. This conjugate was not observed in either the dog or man.

GLYCOLS

Although ethylene glycol does not appear to form a glucuronoside, Miura (283) isolated a glucuronoside of propylene glycol as its barium salt from the urine of rabbits and suggested the formula, $CH_3CHOHCH_2O \cdot C_6H_9O_6$. It has been demonstrated more recently that propylene glycol, perfused through cat liver, causes a deposition of glycogen (309) indicating partial utilization by the body. 2,3-Butylene glycol has been reported to form a conjugate with glucuronic acid in the rabbit (303). Pinacol, $(CH_3)_2COHCOH(CH_3)_2$, also appears to be excreted as a glucuronoside by the rabbit (419).

ALIPHATIC ALDEHYDES

Neubauer (299) found no significant increase in the excretion of glucuronosides following administration of isobutyraldehyde, isovaleraldehyde or heptaldehyde. These unsubstituted aliphatic aldehydes are probably oxidized to the corresponding acids, which then undergo the usual β-oxidation. Halogenated aldehydes, however, apparently are oxidized only with difficulty. Chloral hydrate, $CCl_3CH(OH)_2$, as previously mentioned, was found by Mering and Musculus (258) to form urochloralic acid, which Jaffe (183) suggested might be a derivative of his newly discovered acid, $C_6H_{10}O_7$, a fact later confirmed by Mering (256) and Külz (211). The latter investigator showed that urochloralic acid was a compound of trichloroethyl alcohol and glucuronic acid (m.p. 142°; $[\alpha]_D$ −65.2° (Na salt)) and was the main product of chloral hydrate metabolism in man, dog and rabbit. Unlike its precursor, urochloralic acid is devoid of hypnotic action. Butyl chloral hydrate, $CH_3CHClCCl_2CH(OH)_2$, similarly forms a urobutylchloralic acid (211) which presumably is 2,2,3-trichlorobutyl glucuronoside, $CH_3CHClCCl_2CH_2OC_6H_9O_6$. Bromal hydrate also forms a glucuronic acid derivative (235) which appeared to be analogous to urochloralic acid and was detected by the same method (429).

ALIPHATIC KETONES

The metabolism of aliphatic ketones requires more complete investigation. However, indications are that many of these are partly reduced to the corresponding secondary alcohols and excreted as glucuronosides. Neubauer (299) found that increased glucuronic acid excretion resulted from feeding methyl ethyl, methyl propyl, methyl isopropyl, diethyl, methyl butyl, methyl *tert*-butyl (pinacoline), ethyl propyl, ethyl isopropyl and methyl hexyl ketones to dogs. Mesityl oxide and acetylacetone also were reported to form glucuronosides. As mentioned before, however, Neubauer's analytical methods were not as reliable as later procedures. Dichloroacetone is reduced and excreted as dichloroisopropyl glucuronoside (411). A conjugated glucuronic acid also is excreted after administration of cyclohexanone (74). Only one report was found where a glucuronoside formed from a ketone has been isolated; Saneyoshi (373) obtained the barium salt of *sec*-butyl glucuronoside from the urine of rabbits that had been fed methyl ethyl ketone.

II. Phenols

Because of their importance in medical science, the metabolism of phenols has been the subject of numerous investigations. When phenol itself is fed to rabbits, about 90 per cent is excreted as phenylglucuronoside and phenylsulfuric acid (331). Oxidation products account for most of the remaining 10 per cent; only traces of free phenol are excreted. The products of oxidation, catechol, hydroquinone (18) and 1,2,4-benzenetriol, occurring only in small amounts, are excreted as ethereal sulfates (116). Part of the dose always remained unaccounted for and it was assumed that this fraction was oxidized. Williams (439) showed that when small doses of phenol are fed to rabbits, ethereal sulfate conjugation accounts for the larger part of combined phenol eliminated. As the dose was increased, the percentage combined with sulfate decreased rapidly and glucuronic acid conjugation became more pronounced. Thus it appears that there is a limit beyond which elimination of phenol is taken over by the glucuronic acid mechanism, apparently acting in a reserve protective capacity. Deichmann (71) found that detoxication by conjugation had definitely started within 1 to 3 minutes after oral administration of a lethal dose of phenol to rabbits. This was indicated by the presence of conjugated phenol in the liver and kidneys.

Phenyl glucuronoside (m.p. 150–151° and $[\alpha]_D$ −82° in water) was isolated by Külz (212) in 1883 and by Salkowski and Neuberg (368) in 1906. The compound was synthesized by Neuberg and Niemann (306). In the rabbit the greater portion of injected phenyl glucuronoside is excreted unchanged, but when fed, the amount appearing in the urine is reduced by one-half and there is a rise in the excretion of ethereal sulfates (116, 292). Williams (447) assumed from these findings that phenyl glucuronoside must be partly or wholly hydrolyzed in the intestine and the liberated phenol again conjugated before excretion. The conjugation of phenol appeared to be influenced by a number of factors such as nature of the diet, fatigue and temperature. The influence of different types of food upon the fate of phenol apparently is not due to the acidic or basic character of the foods but mainly, if not entirely, to the effect of the type of food on amount of urine excreted (40, 41). Fatigue (324) causes a reduction in the ability of rabbits to conjugate and oxidize phenol. Although Williams (439) investigated the effect of ring substituents on the conjugation of phenol with sulfuric acid in the rabbit, no reports were found on the influence of substitution on glucuronic acid conjugation or on oxidation of phenol.

Cresols are eliminated by the dog partly as glucuronosides and ethereal sulfates (305, 332) and considerable portions are oxidized. o-Cresol (X) is oxidized to a slight extent to a substance thought to be methylhydroquinone (XI). Salicylic acid, a possible metabolite, was not found. p-Cresol (XII) was also partly oxidized, but in this case the side chain was attacked producing p-hydroxybenzoic acid (XIII).

Neuberg and Kretschner (305) isolated a barium double salt ($[\alpha]_D -34.5°$) of p-tolyl glucuronoside and p-tolyl sulfuric acid (XIV) from the urine of dogs fed p-cresol. They formulated the salt as follows:

$$CH_3 \bigcirc O-CH(CHOH)_3 \overset{\overset{\displaystyle O}{\frown}}{CHCOO}-Ba-OSO_2O \bigcirc CH_3$$

XIV

Halogenated phenols, used in the past as external disinfectants, now appear to act also as powerful internal disinfectants. Their administration has been reported to effect sterilization of the urine and to render the blood bacteriostatic (454, 455). p-Chlorophenol is excreted in conjugation with sulfuric acid and probably with glucuronic acid, judging from the reducing value of the urine. It is reported that 3,5-dimethylchlorophenol (XV) and p-chloro-m-cresol (XVI) also have bacteriostatic properties in the body and that the portion of these compounds excreted in the free state may be regulated by changing the pH of the urine through administration of sodium bicarbonate or ammonium chloride (456). On a normal diet man was found to excrete about 31 per cent of injected 3,5-dimethylchlorophenol in a combined form, 14 per cent as a glucuronoside and 17 per cent as a sulfate.

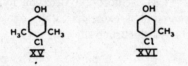

The cyanophenyl glucuronosides have been prepared biosynthetically by feeding the corresponding cyanophenols to rabbits (399). Only β-p-cyano-phenyl glucuronoside was isolated as such, the monohydrate forming color-less needles (m.p. 140° (decomp.), $[\alpha]_D^{20}$ −92). The o- and p-glucuronosides were obtained as crystalline amides and triacetyl methyl esters.

The relation between conjugation and deamination of p-hydroxybenzyl-amine and related phenolic compounds in the rabbit was investigated by Hartles and Williams (147). Their results indicated that the extent of glucuronic acid conjugation was inversely proportional to the rate of de-amination with phenolic amines of the type studied. Percentages of the compounds fed which were excreted as glucuronosides were as follows: N-(p-hydroxybenzyl)acetamide (XVII), 60; (p-hydroxybenzyl)methyl-amine (XVIII), 54; p-hydroxybenzylamine (XIX), 30; p-hydroxybenzal-dehyde (XX), 33; and p-hydroxybenzoic acid (XXI), 18.

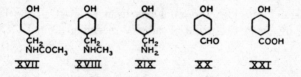

Polyhydric phenols are conjugated in a manner similar to phenol itself, forming ethereal sulfates and glucuronosides, but, in most cases, only one of the phenolic hydroxyls is conjugated and the glucuronosides and ethereal sulfates excreted contain free phenolic hydroxyl groups (447). After feed-ing resorcinol (XXII), Külz (213) isolated the corresponding glucuronoside as its barium salt. He also obtained an impure preparation of hydroqui-none glucuronoside after feeding hydroquinone (XXIII). Garton and Williams (115) isolated and characterized the monoglucuronosides of hy-droquinone and resorcinol as the crystalline methyl esters of the corre-sponding acetoxyphenyl triacetylglucuronosides. Some 43 per cent of the former and 52 per cent of the latter were excreted as glucuronosides, when fed. Ethereal sulfate conjugates appeared in smaller amounts. Neither phenol was found to be oxidized to trihydric phenols or other substances.

When catechol (XXIV) was fed (114) 70 per cent of the dose was excreted as a monoglucuronoside.   About 87 per cent of 4-chlorocatechol fed to rabbits was excreted as 4-chloro-2-hydroxyphenyl glucuronoside (86). Similarly, 4-chlororesorcinol is excreted to the extent of 78 per cent as 4-chloro-3-hydroxyphenyl glucuronoside.

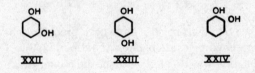

Adrenaline (XXV) is related to catechol and the naturally occurring (levorotatory) form, which is the adrenal hormone, finds extensive use in medicine.   Dodgson, Garton and Williams (85, 86) questioned the conclusion of Deichmann (70) that *l*-adrenaline is excreted by rabbits wholly as a sulfate and not as a glucuronoside and showed that about 21 per cent of *d*-adrenaline is excreted as a glucuronoside, the amount excreted as a sulfate being insignificant.

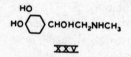

A monoglucuronoside of orcinol has been isolated as the barium salt ($[\alpha]_D$ $-73.6°$) from the urine of rabbits receiving orcinol (XXVI) (389, 390).

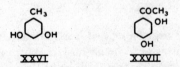

Dogs that had ingested 2,4-dihydroxyacetophenone (XXVII) excreted the monoglucuronoside of this compound, which was isolated both in the free state (decomp. 170°) and as a copper salt, $C_{14}H_{14}O_9Cu \cdot 4H_2O$; the po-

sition of conjugation was not established (297).   The monoglucuronoside of phloroglucinol (XXVIII) has been isolated from the urine of rabbits as a barium salt and subsequently converted to the potassium salt ($[\alpha]_D$ −80.8°) (390). Gallacetophenone (XXIX) also forms a glucuronoside (297).

A glucuronoside isolated as a dichloro derivative by Blum (31) in 1892 is one of the products of thymol metabolism in man. He treated urine from patients receiving thymol with concentrated hydrochloric acid and sodium hypochlorite and, on standing, the dichlorothymyl glucuronoside separated as large needles. The same compound also has been obtained by similar treatment of urine from thymol-treated dogs and rabbits (198, 413). Blum formulated it as 2,4-dichloro-3-methyl-6-isopropylphenyl glucuronoside (XXX).

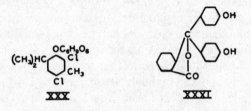

Interest in the metabolism of phenolphthalein (XXXI) was stimulated by the discovery of its purgative action on the animal organism. Both this compound and its tetrachloro derivative are excreted by dogs as conjugates (1) which appeared to be sulfates and glucuronosides (107). Although the two phenolic hydroxyl groups of phenolphthalein are attached to different aromatic rings, only one group was conjugated. Di Somma (80) isolated phenolphthalein monoglucuronoside from rabbit urine as a cinchonidine salt which crystallized with one molecule of alcohol or dioxane of crystallization, depending upon the solvent employed. The alcoholate, $C_{45}H_{44}O_{11}N_2 \cdot C_2H_5OH$ is levorotatory ($[\alpha]_D$ −64.5° in 80 per cent alcohol). Only about 45 per cent of the administered drug could be recovered, which was taken to indicate degradation of a large proportion in the body.

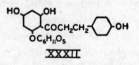

Phloridzin (XXXII) is a phenolic glucoside of phloretin. When administered to animals orally or subcutaneously, both phloridzin and its aglucone, phloretin, give rise to an intense glycosuria without an accompanying hyperglycemia; the blood-sugar level is in fact diminished and the renal threshold for sugar is abolished.   The metabolism of phloridzin is therefore of interest.   Schüller (382) isolated from the urine of phloridzin-injected rabbits a crystalline substance which was shown to be phloridzin glucuronoside ($[\alpha]_D$ −102.2° in water).   On partial hydrolysis with dilute sulfuric acid it gave glucose and phloretin glucuronoside.   The latter compound could be further hydrolyzed to phloretin and glucuronic acid.   It was thus shown that phloridzin glucuronoside contained both the original glucose molecule and glucuronic acid.   He showed that conjugation with glucuronic acid alters the effect of phloridzin on the excretion of sugar, for whereas 1.3 g. of phloridzin glucuronoside injected into a dog caused the excretion of 3–5 g. of glucose in 24 hrs., the equivalent amount of phloridzin caused the excretion of 20 g. or more.   Williams (447) takes this as evidence that the formation of phloridzin glucuronoside causes partial detoxication of phloridzin and that the action of phloridzin on the kidney must be due mainly to the unconjugated glucoside.

Both α- and β-naphthols are converted to glucuronosides and ethereal sulfates in the body and also probably are oxidized to a slight extent (220). Both glucuronosides were isolated from urine.   α-Naphthyl β-glucuronoside is a crystalline solid (m.p. 202–3°, $[\alpha]_D$ −89.3°) and also was formed during metabolism of naphthalene.   β-Naphthyl β-glucuronoside crystallizes as a hydrate (m.p. 100°, $[\alpha]_D$ −90.65°; in the anhydrous state, m.p. 151°, $[\alpha]_D$ −100.85°) (24).

III. Aromatic Hydrocarbons

Benzene is oxidized *in vivo* to phenolic compounds (290, 383) which are conjugated partially with sulfuric acid and partially with glucuronic acid before excretion (331).   Only when large doses are administered is any unchanged benzene excreted (88) although some may be eliminated by way of the lungs (217, 298).   The side-chain of ethylbenzene is oxidized *in vivo* and, along with benzoic and mandelic acids, some methyl phenyl carbinol, $C_6H_5CHOHCH_3$, is formed and excreted in combination with glucuronic acid (299, 418).   All three xylenes are primarily oxidized in the rabbit to the corresponding toluic acids (43).   Thirty per cent of the *o*-xylene fed is reported to be excreted as an ester glucuronoside, with 10 to 15 per cent more excreted as an ether-type glucuronoside; the latter presumably results from hydroxylation of the xylene.   The corresponding toluic acids from *m*- and *p*-xylenes are excreted chiefly as glycine conjugates, only very small amounts being conjugated with glucuronic acid.

Williams (447) concludes from the available evidence that the most probable metabolic pathway of bromobenzene is simultaneous conjugation and oxidation, the primary products being p-bromophenylcysteine and p-bromophenol. He states that secondary reactions may involve acetylation of the bromophenylcysteine and conjugation of bromophenol with sulfuric and glucuronic acids. Chlorobenzene gives rise to a substance which appears to be a glucuronoside in addition to sulfur compounds (17). Coombs and Hele (56) found that a larger proportion of these compounds was conjugated with glucuronic acid by pigs than by dogs.

The disposition of naphthalene in the animal organism is of interest because repeated doses of this compound produce opacity of the crystalline lens of rabbits. There is a close histological resemblance between this condition and human senile cataract. Several investigators have observed indications of a rise in glucuronic acid content of the urine following administration of naphthalene to dogs or rabbits (35, 93, 219), and Lesnik (219) obtained a small amount of α-naphthyl glucuronoside from the urine of a dog that had ingested 12 g. of naphthalene. Other products of naphthalene metabolism were naphthylmercapturic acid, an unidentified substance giving free naphthalene when acidified "naphthalene urine" was distilled, and possibly naphthyl ethereal sulfate.

The fate of tetrahydronaphthalene (tetralin) in the body is not yet clear. Pohl and Rawicz (330) reported that rabbits, dogs and humans, after receiving this compound, excreted tetrahydronaphthyl glucuronoside, a dihydronaphthalene of unknown constitution and naphthalene. Röckemann (366) found a different glucuronoside in dog urine and in rabbit urine. He suggested that rabbits probably excrete the β-tetralyl glucuronoside (XXXIII), an uncrystallizable syrup which gives the corresponding dextrorotatory β-tetralol on hydrolysis; β-tetralol is converted only with difficulty into dihydronaphthalene. From the glucuronoside obtained from dog urine he isolated the α-tetralol (XXXIV), which is readily converted

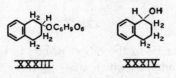

XXXIII   XXXIV

into dihydronaphthalene. Whether all products of tetralin metabolism which have been reported are formed *in vivo* or whether some are artifacts of the isolation procedures must be decided by further investigation.

Phenanthrene metabolism deserves more attention since this ring system forms the basic nucleus of many biologically important compounds including the sex hormones and sterols. Bergell and Pschorr (23) in 1903 showed that urine obtained from rabbits after feeding phenanthrene was strongly levorotatory.   They believed that phenanthrene was oxidized to a phenanthrol, which was excreted as a phenanthryl glucuronoside.   Later work with rats showed that, along with an increase in glucuronic acid excretion, there occurred an increased excretion of neutral and ethereal sulfur following injection of phenanthrene (93).

Boyland and Levi (37, 38) investigated the metabolism of anthracene very thoroughly and isolated two different crystalline glucuronosides, one from rabbit urine and the other from rat urine.   That from rabbits was shown to be a 1,2-dihydroxy-1,2-dihydroanthracene-1-glucuronoside, m.p. 197°, $[\alpha]_D$ +197° (in dioxane), while that from rat urine appeared to be the levorotatory isomer, $[\alpha]_D$ −114° (in dioxane), m.p. 199–200°.

The metabolism of 3,4-benzpyrene, a hydrocarbon of extremely high carcinogenic activity which has been isolated from coal tar, is by no means clear.   However, one metabolic product has been isolated in crystalline form from bile (52) and identified as 8-hydroxy-3,4-benzpyrene (22) (XXXV).   3,4-Benzpyrene-5,8-quinone (XXXVI) was isolated from the faeces of rats receiving 3,4-benzpyrene (22).   Other hydroxy compounds, some phenolic and others alcoholic in nature, have been suggested as intermediary metabolites of benzpyrene (434).   Although glucuronosides of these compounds have not been reported, a slight rise in glucuronic acid excretion following administration of 3,4-benzpyrene has been observed (93).   Interest is aroused by an isolated observation that oral or parenteral administration of small repeated doses of sodium glucuronate seemed to have appreciable inhibiting action on the development of cancer produced by application of benzpyrene to the skin of mice (230).

XXXV   XXXVI   XXXVII

Metabolism of fluorene in the rabbit results in both 2-hydroxyfluorene (XXXVII) and a compound which analyzes correctly for a hydrate of its glucuronoside, m.p. 214–215° (294).

IV. Aromatic Acids

Glucuronic acid appears to play an important role in the metabolism of aromatic acids; many of these are excreted in combination with glucuronic acid as well as with glycine by all species except the fowl.   The proportion in which these two conjugations occur seems to be dependent to a large

extent upon the chemical nature of other substituents present in addition
to the carboxyl group.   The nature as well as quantity of metabolites also
appears to vary with species.   Conjugation of glutamine with phenylacetic
acid in man and the higher apes, and ornithine synthesis in birds, represent
additional detoxication mechanisms in certain species.   Variable quantities
of aromatic acids also may be excreted uncombined and the aromatic nucleus may suffer some oxidation *in vivo* with the formation of small amounts
of phenolic acids.

Benzoic acid can conjugate with both glycine and glucuronic acid.
Herbivorous animals appear to excrete benzoic acid almost entirely as
hippuric acid, whereas carnivores may excrete more benzoyl glucuronoside
than hippuric acid.   Large doses of benzoic acid cause excretion of appreciable amounts of benzoyl glucuronoside by man (347), the ram (228), and
the pig (63), but man is able to excrete smaller doses entirely as hippuric
acid (66).   In the dog, apparently the only carnivorous animal studied,
conjugation with glucuronic acid plays the more important role, formation
of hippuric acid after ingestion of benzoic acid being relatively small and
comparatively fixed (340), but this does not seem to be true for the synthesis of phenaceturic acid.   Quick (348, 349) has attempted to explain
this phenomenon, which apparently is peculiar to this species, on the basis
that in this case hippuric acid synthesis occurs only in the kidney, whereas
it also takes place elsewhere in other animals.   Quick believes that absorbed benzoic acid probably first is converted in the liver to benzoyl glucuronoside which then passes by way of the blood stream to the kidney.
In the latter organ some of the glucuronoside, depending upon its rate of
excretion, is hydrolyzed and the resulting free benzoic acid combines with
glycine.   The chances are, therefore, that more glucuronoside than hippuric acid will be excreted.   He found that in other animals hippuric acid
and benzoyl glucuronoside are formed simultaneously and in similar
amounts.   Phenaceturic acid synthesis, however, was not confined to the
kidney in the dog and hence more of this acid was excreted as glycine conjugate than as glucuronoside.

So-called benzoyl glucuronic acid was first isolated from the urine of
sheep by Magnus-Levy (228), who obtained it as a strychnine salt and as
an amorphous dextrorotatory sodium salt.   He assigned to it the structure
of a 1-benzoyl glucuronic acid, without experimental evidence to support
this formula.   Quick (341) isolated a crystalline levorotatory benzoyl derivative of glucuronic acid from the urine of dogs.   This compound changed
rotation rapidly in the presence of alkali, reduced common sugar reagents
and appeared to combine with sodium cyanide.   These facts led Quick to

believe that the aldehyde group of the glucuronic acid was free and that the benzoyl radical was attached to a carbon atom other than the first. He favored a 2-benzoyl glucuronic acid structure. Pryde and Williams (333) pointed out that the properties of benzoyl glucuronic acid were consistent with the 1-benzoyl structure of Magnus-Levy and that the observations of Quick could all be explained by alkali-lability of the ester linkage joining the benzoyl radical to the glucosidic carbon atom of glucuronic acid. The structure was definitely established by Goebel (122), who demonstrated that the methyl ester of 1-benzoyl 2,3,4-triacetylglucuronoside prepared by synthesis was identical with that prepared from natural benzoyl glucuronoside. Difference in rotation between the levorotatory acid of Quick and the dextrorotatory sodium salt of Magnus-Levy was explained by Goebel on the basis that the salt was isolated from an alkaline urine which had stood for some time, and that a stereochemical rearrangement of the levorotatory benzoyl glucuronoside probably had occurred.

Glucuronic acid conjugation is influenced by the nature of substituent groups, acidic groups in the *ortho* and *para* position of benzoic acid tending to diminish, whereas basic groups tend to increase the output of glucuronoside; neutral groups in these positions have little influence. Groups substituted in the *meta* position have little effect on glucuronoside formation but any effect tends to be opposite to that of *ortho* substitution. These generalizations were made by Quick (350), who studied the mechanism only in the dog. He found that the following monosubstituted aromatic acids caused excretion of glucuronosides in various animals: *o*-, *m*-, *p*-toluic acid; *o*-, *m*-, *p*-chlorobenzoic acid; *o*-, *m*-, *p*-bromobenzoic acid; *o*-iodobenzoic acid; *o*-, *m*-, *p*-hydroxybenzoic acid; *o*-, *m*-, *p*-aminobenzoic acid; *m*-, *p*-nitrobenzoic acid. More recently Bray, Thorpe and Wood (46) have studied the glucuronogenic activity of the toluic acids and their amides in rabbits.

The metabolism of salicylic acid (*o*-hydroxybenzoic acid) is of particular interest because of its use as a therapeutic agent, particularly in rheumatic diseases. A salicylic acid-glucuronic acid conjugate is one of the products excreted following ingestion of this compound. The possible occurrence of such conjugates was first reported by Baldoni (15) in 1905 and their occurrence in "salicylic acid" urine was reported by Neuberg (302) and Quick (350). None of these investigators succeeded in isolating a pure compound. Kapp and Coburn (194) produced evidence that glucuronic acid may be attached to either the phenolic or carboxylic group of the salicylic acid molecule. Galimard (113) reported that part of the salicylic acid was excreted in combination with one mole and part with two moles of glucuronic acid. Following administration of salicylates, patients suffering from rheumatic fever excreted conjugated glucuronic acid in amounts within the range observed for normal subjects, although the output of salicyluric was less and that of gentisic acid much larger than normal (194). Quick (351) found that m-hydroxybenzoic acid is excreted by man largely in combination with glycine, but a small amount is conjugated with glucuronic acid. The amount of glucuronoside formed from p-hydroxybenzoic acid was extremely small in man. He found that the main conjugation product in the dog is a compound containing two glucuronic acid residues, one attached to the aromatic ring through its phenolic hydroxyl and the other through its carboxyl group. This compound, p-glucuronosidobenzoyl glucuronoside (XXXVIII), formed white needles (melting with decomp. slightly above 200°) that were levorotatory. Its exact structure and the configuration of its glycoside linkages were not established but both linkages were believed to be of the β-type.

$$\text{HOOCCH-(CHOH)}_3\text{-CHO} \underset{\text{XXXVIII}}{\bigcirc} \text{COOCH-(CHOH)}_3\text{-CHCOOH}$$

When ingested by man this diglucuronoside was hydrolyzed and the resulting p-hydroxybenzoic acid was slowly eliminated both free and conjugated as p-hydroxyhippuric acid.

The major metabolites isolated following the administration of salicylamide (o-hydroxybenzamide) and of m-hydroxybenzamide to rabbits (45) were 2-carbamylphenyl glucuronoside (m.p. 175–176° (decomp.)), and 3-carbamylphenyl glucuronoside (m.p. 163–164° (decomp.)), respectively. Gentisamide also was isolated following ingestion of salicylamide. p-Hydroxybenzamide is converted in rabbits (44) to 4-carbamylphenyl glucuronoside (m.p. 212° (decomp.)).

Dogs excrete a large portion of ingested anthranilic acid (o-aminobenzoic acid) as a glucuronoside (282). Some 72 per cent of anthranilic acid may be excreted by the dog as a glucuronoside within 12 hrs. and 50 per cent of an ingested dose of m-aminobenzoic acid also is excreted in combination with glucuronic acid (350); a considerable portion (60–70 per cent) of p-aminobenzoic acid likewise is excreted as glucuronoside.

In the lower animals the metabolism of phenylacetic acid is qualitatively similar but quantitatively dissimilar to that of benzoic acid, the compound being excreted as glycine and glucuronic acid conjugates. Quick (344), working with dogs, found that almost twice as much phenylacetic acid was excreted combined with glycine as with glucuronic acid.   Glutamine takes the place of glycine in the metabolism of phenylacetic acid by man; a small amount of phenylacetyl glucuronoside is excreted but, after a single dose of phenylacetic acid, 95 per cent is excreted as phenylacetyl glutamine and 5 per cent as the glucuronoside.   On continued ingestion of the acid there is a tendency for more to be excreted as the glucuronoside (5).

Diphenylacetic acid is not metabolized by man in the same way as phenylacetic acid, the only conjugate found being diphenylacetyl glucuronoside (decomp. at 180–185°; $[\alpha]_D$ −34.75°) (XXXIX); the same conjugation occurs in the rabbit and the dog (281).

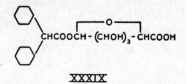

XXXIX

The nature of the metabolic end products of the higher homologues of phenylacetic acid is dependent upon the number of carbon atoms in the aliphatic chain, which is degraded through β-oxidation to benzoic or phenylacetic acid, depending upon whether the chain contains an odd or even number of carbon atoms.   These oxidation products are conjugated and excreted in the same way as when the acids themselves are fed.

When protocatechuic acid (3,4-dihydroxybenzoic acid) (XL) was administered to rabbits, some 30 per cent appeared to be conjugated, about 10 per cent as glucuronoside; the remainder was excreted unchanged (86). The glucuronoside was not isolated so its structure is not known.   The monomethyl ether, vanillic acid (4-hydroxy-3-methoxybenzoic acid) (XLI) behaved similarly; about one-half was excreted in the free state and one-fourth was conjugated (371).   Of the portion conjugated, about two-thirds appeared as glucuronovanillic acid (o-methoxy-p-carboxyphenyl glucuronoside).   Thus vanillic acid does not form a glucuronoside through its carboxyl group and is therefore unlike most aromatic acids.

The monomethyl and dimethyl ethers of protocatechuic acid (XL) are metabolized in entirely different manners by the rabbit, presumably because vanillic acid contains a free hydroxyl group whereas in veratric acid (3,4-dimethoxybenzoic acid) (XLII) this hydroxyl is blocked by a methyl group.   Vanillic acid conjugates through the phenolic hydroxyl while veratric acid conjugation is confined to the carboxyl group at the opposite end of the molecule.   Sammons and Williams (372) found that 41 per cent of the veratric acid ingested by rabbits was excreted in the free state and that 20–29 per cent was conjugated. All of the combined veratric acid appeared in the urine as veratroyl glucuronoside (m.p. 169–70°; $[\alpha]_D$ −13.1° in water), a compound very similar to benzoyl glucuronoside in properties.

Piperonylic acid (3,4-methylenedioxybenzoic acid) (XLIII) when fed to rabbits produces a reducing urine and this was taken as an indication that a glucuronoside (piperonylyl glucuronoside) is excreted (447); a glycine conjugate, piperonylylglycine, also was formed. Piperonylic acid apparently is produced and excreted as such during the metabolism of safrole (XLIV) and isosafrole (XLV) in the dog (150).

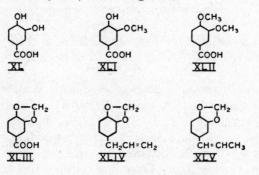

α-Naphthoic acid is conjugated with glucuronic acid to an appreciable extent by the dog but only small amounts of the glycine conjugate are formed; in this respect it behaves like an *ortho*-substituted benzoic acid (350). β-Naphthoic acid formed no conjugate in the dog although in the rabbit a small amount of β-naphthuric acid was produced.

V. Aromatic Alcohols, Ethers, Aldehydes and Ketones

Primary aromatic alcohols appear to be oxidized *in vivo* either to benzoic acid or phenylacetic acid depending upon the length of the side-chain. Thus benzyl alcohol forms benzoic acid and phenylethyl alcohol produces phenylacetic acid (447). Primary aromatic alcohols substituted in the ring behave similarly, saligenin (*o*-hydroxybenzyl alcohol) having been found to form salicylic acid in the body (295). Although direct formation of glucuronosides from the alcohols has not been observed, this probably occurs in some cases, since the *o*-nitrobenzyl alcohol formed during metabolism of *o*-nitrotoluene is excreted as *o*-nitrobenzyl glucuronoside (183).

Although secondary aromatic alcohols apparently have not been studied directly, something of their metabolism is known since they are formed from aromatic ketones *in vivo*.   Because of their branched chain, secondary aromatic alcohols undoubtedly are oxidized with greater difficulty than the primary alcohols.   Judging by the behavior of acetophenone, of which some 36 per cent is excreted by the rabbit as the glucuronoside of phenyl methyl carbinol (418), a large proportion of the secondary alcohols formed through reduction of ketones probably is conjugated and excreted as glucuronosides (447).

Aromatic ethers could undergo two types of change in the body: (1) oxidation of the aromatic ring, thereby producing a phenolic ether, and/or, (2) splitting of the ether linkage to produce a phenol.   The only aromatic ether that has been reported to form a conjugate of glucuronic acid is phenetole (ethyl phenyl ether).   After feeding phenetole to dogs, Kossel (206, 207) isolated from the urine a compound which he showed was probably the glucuronoside of *p*-ethoxyphenol.   The structure of this conjugate was later confirmed by Lehmann (218).   The ethereal sulfate of *p*-ethoxyphenol is also formed (209).

Aromatic aldehydes are oxidized *in vivo* almost completely to aromatic acids which are excreted partly as the free acids and partly as conjugates with glycine or glucuronic acid.   When fed to rabbits, *p*-dimethylaminobenzaldehyde not only was oxidized to the corresponding acid, *p*-dimethylaminobenzoic acid being isolated from the urine as a glucuronoside, but was also partially demethylated.   There was evidence that a glucuronic acid conjugate of *p*-monomethylaminobenzoic acid also was formed (186).

Dogs excrete *p*-hydroxybenzaldehyde (XLVI) as *p*-glucuronosidobenzoyl glucuronoside, *p*-hydroxyhippuric acid and possibly free *p*-hydroxybenzoic acid (67, 351).   In the case of rabbits, however, *p*-glucuronosidobenzaldehyde has been isolated from the urine as the 2,4-dinitrophenylhydrazone and it appeared probable that conjugation of the phenolic hydroxyl with glucuronic acid preceded oxidation of the aldehyde group (147).

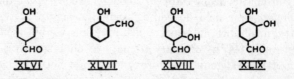

Salicylaldehyde (XLVII) and 2,4-dihydroxybenzaldehyde (XLVIII) are partly excreted unchanged, while protocatechuic aldehyde (3,4-dihydroxybenzaldehyde) (XLIX) is excreted in part as a glucuronosidobenzaldehyde (447).

The chief metabolite of salicylaldehyde in the rabbit is salicylic acid (67).

Baumgarten (19) has reported that the aldehyde is mainly excreted unchanged by human beings, but Williams (447) considers this unlikely.

Vanillin behaves as a typical phenolic aldehyde, being excreted partly as glucuronosidovanillin (L). When vanillin was fed to a rabbit, 69 per cent was oxidized to vanillic acid derivatives, both free and combined, and 14 per cent was excreted as unoxidized but conjugated vanillin (371). Glucuronosidovanillin was assumed to be a precursor of the main conjugated oxidation product, glucuronosidovanillic acid (LI).

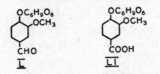

A small amount of the oxidation product was conjugated as an ethereal sulfate.

Syringaldehyde (LII) is converted in rabbits to a glucuronoside having two carboxyl groups, probably 3,5-dimethoxy-4-glucuronosidobenzoic acid (LIII), the glucuronoside of syringic acid (447).

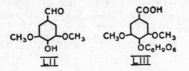

p-Tolualdehyde, anisaldehyde, veratraldehyde, piperonal, and o- and p-aminobenzaldehyde are all oxidized to the corresponding acids, which form conjugates of glucuronic acid in the rabbit (150, 372).

Mixed ketones follow two courses of metabolism in the animal body. In part the carbonyl group is reduced to a secondary alcohol which usually is excreted in combination with glucuronic acid. Another part is oxidized to aromatic acids, but the mechanism of oxidation and nature of the products are the subject of some debate. Dakin stated that if the side-chain to which the keto group is attached contains an odd number of carbon atoms, benzoic acid is formed, whereas phenylacetic acid is produced if the side-chain contains an even number of carbons. Dakin (64, 65) and Hermanns (157) reported that benzyl methyl ketone, $C_6H_5CH_2COCH_3$, formed benzoic acid *in vivo*, whereas phenylethyl methyl ketone, $C_6H_5CH_2CH_2COCH_3$, and phenylbutyl methyl ketone, $C_6H_5CH_2CH_2CH_2$-CH_2COCH_3, formed phenylacetic acid. In contrast to this finding, Thierfelder and Daiber (418) claimed that all mixed ketones form benzoic acid in the body, regardless of whether the keto group is attached to the ring or is in the side-chain, and that the number of carbon atoms in the alkyl group has no influence. In only one case, that of benzyl isopropyl ketone, $C_6H_5CH_2COCH(CH_3)_2$, did these latter workers find phenaceturic acid in the urine, and then in only very small amounts. Metabolic behavior of these ketones is apparently somewhat complex and many inconsistencies require clarification.

The first product identified in the urine of dogs that had ingested acetophenone was hippuric acid (296). Later it was shown that a glucuronoside also is formed both in dogs and in rabbits (299, 411). In a more careful investigation acetophenone was injected subcutaneously into rabbits and it was found (418) that 35.7 per cent was reduced to phenyl methyl carbinol and excreted as a glucuronoside, and 24.3 per cent was oxidized to benzoic acid and excreted as hippuric acid. Small amounts of mandelic acid, free phenyl methyl carbinol and unchanged acetophenone were also excreted. The glucuronoside of phenyl methyl carbinol was isolated as a crystalline potassium salt ($[\alpha]_D$ −124.4°). Quick (345) confirmed these results and reported that little if any benzoic acid formed from acetophenone is excreted as benzoyl glucuronoside. The sequence of formation of the various metabolites is not entirely clear but Williams (447) suggests the following:

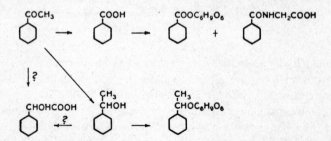

The approximate extent to which some ketones are reduced to carbinols was shown by Thierfelder and Daiber (418) as follows:

Ketone	Percentage Reduced to Carbinol	Rotation of Glucuronoside in Water, $[\alpha]_D$
Acetophenone	35.7, as phenyl methyl carbinol	−124.4° (K salt)
Propiophenone	26, as phenyl ethyl carbinol	−126.08° (K salt)
Benzyl isopropyl ketone	43, as benzyl isopropyl carbinol	−54.9° (K salt)
Butyrophenone	41, as phenyl n-propyl carbinol	−108.7° (Cd salt)

o-Aminoacetophenone behaves in the expected manner in the rabbit, forming the glucuronoside of *o*-aminophenyl methyl carbinol and small amounts of anthranilic acid (180).

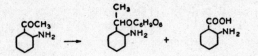

Introduction of hydroxyl groups into the ring of aromatic ketones appears to hinder both oxidation and reduction of the carbonyl group. Phenolic ketones are excreted either unchanged or as glucuronosides and ethereal sulfates. *p*-Hydroxypropiophenone, gallacetophenone and resacetophenone are excreted as conjugated sulfates and glucuronosides by both dogs and rabbits, the keto group remaining unchanged (297).

p-Benzoquinone is reduced to hydroquinone in the dog and rabbit and excreted as the ethereal sulfate and probably also as the glucuronoside (384); its trichloro- and tetrachloro- derivatives behave similarly.

VI. Aromatic Nitrogen Compounds

Many aromatic nitrogen compounds are employed medicinally. Others, manufactured on a large scale in the production of dyes and explosives, constitute a potential health hazard to manufacturing personnel. Glucuronic acid has been shown to play a part in the metabolism of several of these compounds.

Aromatic nitro groups generally are reduced *in vivo* to amino groups. Chemical reduction of the $-NO_2$ group proceeds through formation of nitroso and hydroxylamino groups.

$$-NO_2 \rightarrow -NO \rightarrow -NHOH \rightarrow -NH_2$$

It is probable that the biological reduction follows the same course since the hydroxylamino, although not the nitroso, stage has been observed.

After administration of nitrobenzene, the products found in the urine are small amounts of unchanged nitrobenzene and large amounts of *p*-aminophenol and its conjugates with glucuronic and sulfuric acids (261).

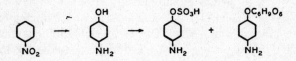

Mechanism of the conversion of nitrobenzene to *p*-aminophenol is still a matter of controversy.

The metabolic behavior of nitrotoluene was studied very early by Jaffe (182, 183). *o*-Nitrotoluene is converted to *o*-nitrobenzyl alcohol and *o*-nitrobenzoic acid in dogs. The alcohol is excreted to the extent of 25 per cent as nitrobenzyl glucuronoside which can be isolated as a complex with urea. *o*-Nitrobenzoic acid is excreted in an amount corresponding to 10 per cent of the dose fed. No *o*-nitrobenzylaldehyde was detected although it may be an intermediate. Some reduction of the nitro group also may occur although this was not reported by Jaffe.

No glucuronoside appears to be produced in the case of *p*-nitrotoluene.

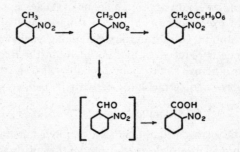

The fate of the high explosive, TNT (2,4,6-trinitrotoluene), in the animal body has been the subject of much investigation, since workers engaged in its manufacture often show toxic symptoms which are sometimes fatal. Channon, Mills and Williams (53) have given a clearer picture of the metabolism of this compound in experimental animals than was presented by earlier workers. Three metabolites, 2,6-dinitro-4-hydroxylaminotoluene, 2,6-dinitro-4-aminotoluene and 2,4-dinitro-6-aminotoluene were isolated from the urine of TNT-fed rabbits. These results show that in this species

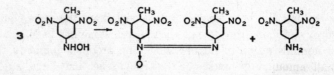

3

at least two of the three nitro groups of TNT can be reduced and that a hydroxylamine is formed as an intermediate in the reduction of the —NO$_2$ group to —NH$_2$. Yield of the 4-amino compound was greater than that of the 6-amino isomer, indicating that the *p*-nitro group is more easily reduced than the two *ortho* groups. Although a number of investigators have claimed the 2,2',6,6'-tetranitro-4,4'-azoxytoluene is a metabolite of TNT, Channon *et al.* presented evidence that it is not present in freshly voided urine but is an artifact produced from the hydroxylamino compound during isolation.

TNT also causes an increased excretion of glucuronic acid and, in rabbits, nearly one-half of the dose administered can be accounted for as a conjugate with glucuronic acid. The nature of the conjugate or conjugates is uncertain but there is some evidence for the existence in the urine of trinitrobenzyl or dinitroaminobenzyl glucuronoside or both. Both dinitrohydroxylaminotoluene and trinitrobenzyl alcohol are tissue poisons and form methemoglobin *in vitro*, the hydroxylamino compound being particularly powerful in this respect. Formation of these compounds may partly explain the toxic effects of TNT.

2,4-Dinitrophenol is the most important of the six dinitrophenols. It is used in the explosives industry and also has been employed in medicine because of its ability to increase cellular respiration by several hundred per cent. It causes a marked increase in the excretion of glucuronic acid (117). Some is reduced to 2-amino-4-nitro-, 2-nitro-4-amino-, and probably 2,4-diaminophenols (134) which may also be excreted combined with glucuronic acid.

Little information is available regarding the fate of the nitrobenzoic acids in the animal body. *p*-Nitrobenzoic acid shows a marked antibacterial action in some experimental streptococcal and pneumococcal infections. Sodium *m*-nitrobenzoate has been reported to possess trypanocidal action. In an early investigation, Bertagnini (26) states that *p*-nitrobenzoic acid is partly excreted as *p*-nitrohippuric acid by man. Quick (350) found only small amounts of glycine and glucuronic acid conjugates in the urine when the *para* acid was fed to dogs but appreciable quantities of both conjugates were found after administration of the *meta* acid. *o*-Nitrobenzoic acid was mainly excreted unchanged. All three nitrobenzoic acids are reduced in the rat to a small extent (205).

The aromatic amino group is characterized by its stability in the animal body. Modifications which it undergoes are comparatively few and it is very difficult to remove from the aromatic ring *in vivo* (447).

The main products of the metabolism of aniline are *p*-aminophenol (380) and *o*-aminophenol (400). Formation of 4-aminoresorcinol has also been reported by Smith and Williams (402); although some ethereal sulfate formation was detected, 70 per cent of the aniline fed to rabbits was excreted as glucuronosides. Two of these, *p*-acetamido- and *p*-aminophenyl glucuronosides, accounting for about 10 to 15 per cent of the aniline fed, were isolated and identified.   These investigators suggested that a labile, un-identified glucuronoside accounts for more than 50 per cent of the dose fed, and that this breaks up readily to give free glucuronic acid (identified by derivatization).   Similar evidence for the presence of a labile glucuronoside was found after feeding o-, m- and p-anisidines (methoxyanilines), p-phene-tidine (p-ethoxyaniline) (403) and phenacetin (p-ethoxyacetanilide) (401). p-Acetamidophenyl glucuronoside also occurred in the urine after phene-tidine was fed (403).   Phenacetin was found to be transformed largely to p-acetamidophenyl glucuronoside and p-acetamidophenylsulfuric acid (401).   Thus recent work has shown that deethylation is the major meta-bolic change undergone by phenacetin, and deacetylation occurs to a very minor extent—contrary to earlier reports indicating deacetylation as the first step in the metabolism of this compound (166, 229, 288).

Formanilide was thought to be excreted by dogs as p-aminophenol (203). Benzoxazolone also was isolated, but Williams (447) believed it to be an artifact formed from o-aminophenol.   He assumed that the formyl group was removed in the course of metabolism and that the resulting aniline was oxidized in both the *ortho* and *para* positions.   The presence of glu-curonic acid in the urine was indicated (203).   The main metabolic product in rabbits was p-aminophenol.

It was originally believed that the analgesic and antipyretic compound acetanilide was largely deacetylated in the body, since p-aminophenol (287) and benzoxazolone (187) (probably an artifact in this case, also (447)), had been isolated from urine, conjugated with glucuronic and sulfuric acids. Mörner (285), however, isolated potassium p-acetamidophenylsulfate from the urine of man as a double salt with potassium ethyl oxalate.   He also obtained a glucuronoside which he was unable to characterize, but which he thought was probably p-acetamidophenyl glucuronoside or p-amino-phenyl glucuronoside.   Smith and Williams (400) later showed that 80 per cent of the dose of acetanilide can be accounted for in the urine as p-acetamidophenyl glucuronoside and p-acetamidophenylsulfuric acid, ex-creted in a ratio of about 6 to 1, and that less than 5 per cent of the dose is deacetylated.

Dimethylaniline was first investigated by Hildebrandt (164), using rab-bits, and he reported that this compound probably first was oxidized to dimethylaniline oxide which then rearranged to dimethylaminophenol.

$$C_6H_5N(CH_3)_2 \rightarrow C_6H_5\overset{O}{N}(CH_3)_2 \longrightarrow (CH_3)_2NC_6H_4OH$$

Later investigation by Horn (171, 172) showed a striking difference be-tween the metabolism of dimethylaniline in different species.   In the rabbit it is partly demethylated, oxidized in the *para* position and excreted in the urine as the glucuronoside of monomethylaminophenol. In the dog, however, dimethylaniline was completely demethylated, oxidized in the *ortho* position and conjugates of *o*-aminophenol were excreted (171). In neither species was dimethylaniline oxide excreted and when this compound was injected it was converted into the same products as dimethylaniline.

The metabolism of diethylaniline differs markedly from that of dimethylaniline in that it is not deethylated in either the dog or the rabbit and in both species oxidation occurs in the *para* position (173). The diethylaminophenol formed in each case is excreted conjugated. Diethylaniline oxide is not an intermediate in this reaction for when it is injected it is for the most part excreted unchanged along with a small amount of *p*-diethylaminophenol.

When dimethyl-*p*-toluidine is fed to rabbits a reducing substance is excreted which probably is *p*-dimethylaminobenzoyl glucuronoside, for *p*-dimethylaminobenzoic acid can be isolated from the urine (162). If the urine is hydrolyzed with acid and distilled, *o*-dimethylaminophenol is produced; this is probably derived from *p*-dimethylamino-*m*-hydroxybenzoic acid (164).

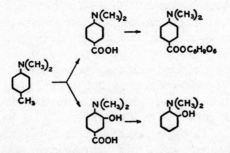

All three aminophenols are excreted as both ethereal sulfates and glucuronosides. The three glucuronosides have been isolated by Williams (445). In the rabbit both the *ortho* and *para* compounds are conjugated to a considerable degree with glucuronic acid and at least 25 per cent of the dose can be obtained as a crystalline glucuronoside. The *para* compound is conjugated with glucuronic acid to a lesser extent than its isomers and a moderate amount is excreted in the free state. All three glucuronosides are levorotatory: *o*-, $[\alpha]_D$ $-76°$; *m*-, $[\alpha]_D$ $-94°$; *p*-, $[\alpha]_D$ $-83°$.

Benzidine is excreted partly unchanged and partly as ethereal sulfate and as glucuronoside (433), which indicates that this compound is partially oxidized *in vivo*, and Adler (2) has stated that a diaminodihydroxybiphenyl of unknown structure is formed. Since the *para* positions are blocked,

Williams (447) believed that the compound formed was probably 3,3'-dihydroxy-4,4'-diaminobiphenyl.

$$H_2N\text{—}\bigcirc\text{—}\bigcirc\text{—}NH_2 \longrightarrow H_2N\underset{OH}{\bigcirc}\text{—}\underset{OH}{\bigcirc}NH_2$$

α-Naphthylamine is stated to be partly excreted unchanged and partly changed to an α-aminonaphthol which is excreted mainly as a conjugate with glucuronic acid and to a small extent with sulfuric acid (447). β-Naphthylamine appears to give rise to bladder tumors in some workers engaged in its manufacture and, for this reason, its metabolism has been more thoroughly investigated than that of the α-isomer. Wiley (438) showed that in the dog β-naphthylamine is oxidized to 2-amino-1-naphthol which he isolated as the acid sulfate. In addition there was an increase in neutral sulfur excretion, indicating that some mercapturic acid may be formed. Using rats, rabbits and monkeys, Dobriner, Hofmann and Rhoads (81) found that, after subcutaneous injection, β-naphthylamine was excreted partly unchanged, partly oxidized and partly acetylated. From the urine they isolated 2-acetamidonaphthalene and 6-acetamido-2-naphthol; it was assumed that the latter compound probably also formed an ethereal sulfate and a glucuronoside. Here again, a difference between the metabolic processes of herbivorous and carnivorous animals is evident (447).

Rats that had been injected with azobenzene produced urines containing aniline, increased amounts of ethereal sulfates and glucuronosides and a compound which, when heated with strong hydrochloric acid, yielded benzidine (94). The precursor of benzidine was assumed to be hydrazobenzene which was suggested as the primary metabolite. Williams (447) suggested that the ethereal sulfate and conjugated glucuronic acid probably result from products of further oxidation of aniline, such as p-aminophenol, and possibly phenolic derivatives of hydrazobenzene.

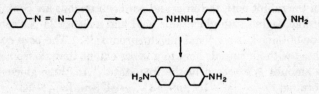

VII. Aromatic Sulfur Compounds (Sulfonamides)

Because of the outstanding importance of certain organic sulfur compounds in the field of medicine, their metabolism is of special interest.

The aromatic sulfonamides are used extensively for the treatment of acute bacterial infections and the discovery of their activity is one of the most important advances in chemotherapy in recent years.

p-Hydroxybenzenesulfonamide, behaving as a typical phenol in the rabbit, is excreted with the sulfonamide group unchanged while the hydroxyl group is conjugated with glucuronic and sulfuric acids. A small portion is oxidized to catechol-4-sulfonamide, which is also excreted conjugated (370). The p-sulfonamidophenyl glucuronoside was isolated as the barium salt ($[\alpha]_D$ $-50°$).

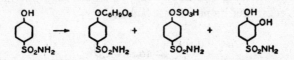

At a dosage level of 0.75 g./kg., 50 per cent was excreted as the glucuronoside and 30 per cent as the sulfate, but with higher doses the total percentage conjugated was less.

Although about 50 per cent of the metanilamide administered is excreted as acetylmetanilamide and another 20 per cent appears as an ethereal sulfate, some glucuronoside also is excreted. The formation of the sulfate and glucuronoside indicate an oxidation of the metanilamide molecule to the phenol, 3-amino-4-hydroxybenzenesulfonamide (82).

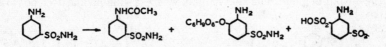

In general, sulfanilamide and its derivatives such as sulfapyridine and sulfathiazole, in which the nuclear amino group is unsubstituted, are partly excreted unchanged, partly acetylated, and partly oxidized to phenolic compounds which may be excreted combined with sulfuric and glucuronic acids, thus (447):

$$H_2N \bigcirc SO_2NHR \rightarrow CH_3CONH \bigcirc SO_2NHR + H_2N \bigcirc SO_2NHR$$

(The position of the —OH group is arbitrary; R = H or another group)

When R represents a group such as pyridine or thiazole it may be oxidized also. The extent to which these drugs are acetylated, oxidized, and

excreted unchanged depends on the nature of the substituent R. Sulfanilamide itself does not appear to form a glucuronic acid conjugate in
rabbits (446), rats (387), or man (120).

Sulfapyridine (LIV), however, is oxidized in the dog to a hydroxysulfa-
pyridine, which is excreted conjugated with glucuronic acid. The silver
salt of this glucuronoside, $C_{11}H_9O_2N_3SAg \cdot OC_6H_8O_6Ag \cdot 3H_2O$, was isolated
by Scudi (385). A compound which appeared to be the glucuronoside
itself was isolated from dog urine by Weber, Lalich and Major (432), who
obtained evidence that the hydroxyl group formed by oxidation *in vivo* is
in the heterocyclic ring and not in the benzenoid ring, but more specific
information regarding its position is lacking.

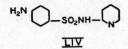

LIV

Nearly 40 per cent of the sulfapyridine administered to the rat is excreted
as a glucuronoside (387); this drug also increases the output of glucuronic
acid in man (120).

Although sulfadiazine (LV) undergoes only very slight oxidation in the
rabbit, both its 4-methyl and 4,6-dimethyl derivatives, sulfamerazine (LVI)
and sulfamezathine (LVII) are more highly acetylated and oxidized in man
and in the rabbit (447).   Both the latter compounds caused a large increase
in the output of glucuronic acid in man, whereas sulfadiazine does not (120).

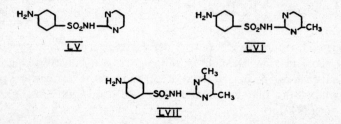

LV   LVI

LVII

A series of publications by Martin and coworkers (240–243, 246) presents
evidence that appears to be somewhat confusing, but from which they drew
the conclusion that simultaneous administration of a number of drugs and
glucuronic acid or its soluble salts resulted in a decrease in toxicity of the
drug itself.   In the case of sulfanilamide, administration of such a mixture
appeared to decrease the extent to which the drug was acetylated.   The
acetylated compound is known to be more toxic than the free base (239).

Martin and Thompson obtained patents (244, 245) on admixtures containing hexuronic acids that were claimed to impart lower toxicity when administered simultaneously with numerous drugs, including sulfonamides.

VIII. Heterocyclic Compounds

Numerous compounds containing heterocyclic nuclei are involved in mammalian metabolism. Some of these are ingested with the food, some result from catabolism of tissue substances and still others are introduced as drugs. Nicotinic acid, vitamins B_1, B_2, B_6 and E, tryptophan, the porphyrins, antipyrine, pyramidone and morphine are examples of this type of compound. It has been shown in a substantial number of cases that ingestion of compounds containing heterocyclic groups results in increased output of glucuronic acid in the urine and, in many cases, definite compounds have been isolated and identified as conjugates of glucuronic acid with either the substance ingested or its metabolic residue. Thus, here again it appears that glucuronic acid is used by the animal organism to rid the system of toxic products or materials that it cannot utilize.

The metabolism of pyridine was first investigated in 1887 by His (168), who found that the compound was oxidized and excreted; the urine gave a reducing test, but no conjugation product could be isolated. He identified the biological oxidation product as methylpyridinium hydroxide, indicating that both oxidation and methylation had occurred. This work was confirmed by Cohn (55).

Vitamin B_6 (pyridoxine) (LVIII) contains the pyridine nucleus and was found to be excreted in large amounts as a conjugate by man and dogs, but not by rats (386). It was inferred that the conjugate contained either

LVIII

glucuronic or sulfuric acid. At least two metabolites were formed, exact structures of which were not known. Neither, however, resembled that formed from unsubstituted pyridine. In one case glucuronic acid appeared to be conjugated with the parent compound through its phenolic hydroxyl group, the structure apparently being otherwise unaltered; similar conjugation with sulfuric acid also occurred. The other metabolite was also conjugated through position 3 but the hydroxymethyl group in position 4 of the parent compound appeared to have been altered in some way.

Quinoline contains a heterocyclic as well as a carbocyclic ring. The former behaves like pyridine in the animal body, undergoing oxidation, methylation and conjugation with glucuronic acid, and results in increased excretion of glucuronic acid (414); output of ethereal sulfate also is increased (112, 414). This ring likewise has a tendency to form a quinone. The carbocyclic ring may behave as a typical benzene ring and be oxidized to phenolic compounds (112, 376). A tendency is reported for the carbocyclic ring to be broken up, leaving the heterocyclic ring to be excreted (87, 314). In dogs and hens quinoline, like pyridine, is methylated and excreted as methylquinolinium hydroxide (414). This latter compound was less toxic than the parent compound to dogs, rabbits and hens and, when fed, was apparently excreted unchanged. However, quinoline did not appear to be methylated by the rabbit but underwent oxidation to a variety of products which probably were conjugated with glucuronic acid and sulfuric acid and excreted.

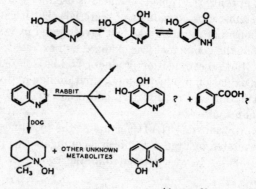

(According to Williams (447))

Hydroxyquinolines, irrespective of whether the hydroxyl group is in the carbocyclic ring as in 8-hydroxyquinoline (39) or in the heterocyclic ring as in 2- or 4-hydroxyquinoline (97), behave in vivo like other phenols, causing an increased output of conjugated glucuronic acid and ethereal sulfate when fed to dogs and rabbits. The glucuronoside of 8-hydroxyquinoline was isolated by Brahm (39) after feeding either 8-hydroxyquinoline or its sulfate "quinolsol"; the glucuronoside is levorotatory, its potassium salt having a specific rotation of about −83.3°.

Karine, the hydrochloride of N-ethyl-8-hydroxy-1,2,3,4-tetrahydroquinoline (LIX) is reported to be excreted as a glucuronoside and as an ethereal sulfate (257).

LIX

Acridine and its derivatives, *e.g.*, acriflavine (trypaflavin or 10-methyl-3,6-diaminoacridinium chloride) (LX) and rivanol (2-ethoxy-6,9-diamino-acridine) (LXI) are reported to be excreted as glucuronosides and ethereal sulfates, indicating oxidation to phenolic substances (393).

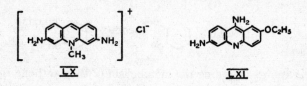

LX   LXI

p-Hydroxybenzylhydantoin (LXII) is conjugated and excreted by the rabbit as a glucuronoside and as ethereal sulfate (179). The glucuronoside is levorotatory, its potassium salt ($KC_{16}H_{17}O_9N_2$) having a specific rotation of $-98°$, and Williams (447) suggested it probably was 5-(*p*-glucuronosido-benzyl)-hydantoin.

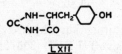

LXII

Indole is oxidized in the animal body to indoxyl or β-hydroxyindole. Indoxyl occurs normally in the urine as an ethereal sulfate but when dogs were fed indole (308) the glucuronoside of indoxyl was isolated from the urine as a barium double salt of indoxyl glucuronoside and indoxyl sulfuric acid (LXIII). The salt was levorotatory and its specific rotation changed in 24 hrs. from $-54.9°$ to $-34°$.

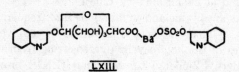

LXIII

Glucuronic acid has been reported (355) to link indoxyl with the peptide chain in urochrome.

3-Hydroxycoumarin is converted almost quantitatively in man to 3-glucuronosidocoumarin (m.p. 207°, $[\alpha]_D$ −72.05°). There is no evidence that the pyrone ring is opened (106). 3-Hydroxycoumarin is the enol form of the lactone of o-hydroxyphenylpyruvic acid but, when fed to rabbits, it behaved in sharp contrast to the acid, which was oxidized largely to o-hydroxyphenylacetic acid.

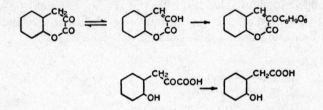

Little is known regarding the metabolism of the xanthone ring, but the fact that Indian yellow, euxanthic acid, is found in the urine of animals is evidence that ingested hydroxyxanthones probably are excreted as conjugates with glucuronic acid (13, 379).

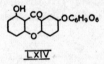

LXIV

Euxanthic acid (2-glucuronosido-8-hydroxyxanthone, m.p. 159–160°; $[\alpha]_D$ −108° in aqueous alcohol) (LXIV) (306) is obtained from the pigment Indian yellow, which is present in the urine of cows that have fed on mango leaves. This pigment was at one time produced in large quantities in Bengal by the simple method of feeding mango leaves to cattle. Production by this means was discouraged because of the deleterious effects on the animals. Euxanthic acid obviously was a detoxication product of euxanthone (2,8-dihydroxyxanthone) or its precursors present in mango leaves. When fed to rabbits, euxanthone is conjugated with glucuronic acid and excreted as euxanthic acid (208).

Drugs such as antipyrine and pyramidone find frequent use in medicine as antipyretics. Glucuronic acid is known to be involved in eliminating these derivatives of the heterocyclic pyrazole ring from the body. Antipyrine (1,5-dimethyl-2-phenyl-3-pyrazolone) (LXV) is converted to hydroxyantipyrine, which is excreted combined with glucuronic and sulfuric acids (214). The glucuronoside was isolated as a levorotatory double salt with barium chloride and had the formula: $(C_{17}H_{19}N_2O_8)_2 \cdot BaCl_2 \cdot H_2O$.

The position of the hydroxyl group in hydroxyantipyrine is not known but Williams (447) suggests that it could be in position 3 of the pyrazolone ring or in some position in the benzene ring.

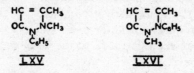

3-Antipyrine (2,5-dimethyl-1-phenyl-3-pyrazolone) (LXVI) is partly conjugated and excreted by dogs, cats and rabbits but the nature of the conjugate is obscure (204).

A small amount of a complex of 4-hydroxyantipyrine with glucuronic acid can be isolated from the urine after ingestion of pyramidone (138). The main products of pyramidone metabolism in man are 4-acetylamino-antipyrine and 4-aminoantipyrine and these two compounds account for about 50 per cent of a 0.5 g. dose. Isolation of a glucuronoside of unknown constitution also was reported by Jaffe (184). In addition the latter investigator isolated rubazonic acid (LXVII) (184) and antipyrylurea (LXVIII) (185). These latter two compounds may have been artifacts (447).

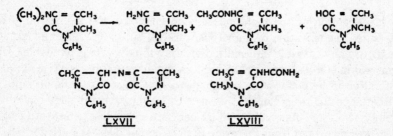

A glucuronoside of leucothionol (21) appears to be excreted by rabbits following oral administration of phenothiazine (LXIX), a compound used in veterinary practice as an anthelmintic. Other products identified were unchanged phenothiazine, leucothionol (LXX) and thionol (LXXI) (420). The latter two compounds apparently constitute a reversible oxidation-

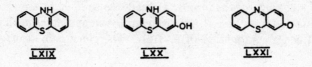

reduction system, thionol being responsible for the reddish coloration of the urine.

According to Oberst (315, 317) a conjugation with glucuronic acid appears to be one of the principal mechanisms involved in the elimination of morphine (LXXII) and its derivatives, heroin (LXXIII) and codeine (LXXIV). In morphine addicts there is a rise in the glucuronic acid output in the urine that is proportional to the dose of the drug.

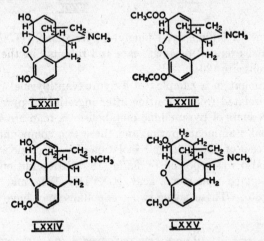

Investigation of the metabolism of morphine in the animal body has attracted the attention of numerous workers, but only within the last few years has any tangible information on the subject become available. Recent work (133) suggests that habituation to morphine may lead to an alteration in its metabolism. It appears that dogs that have become habituated to the drug can destroy it, whereas nontolerant dogs have little ability to do so. As much as 80–92 per cent of the dose, irrespective of its size, was recovered from the urine of nontolerant dogs, the greater part in the conjugated form, but only 35–66 per cent was recovered from habituated animals and only about 30 per cent of this was conjugated. Thus, after tolerance had been established the amount of conjugated morphine excreted was decreased to a greater extent than the amount of free morphine. Conjugation, apparently with glucuronic acid, occurred when morphine was incubated with liver slices of the dog, cat, rat or guinea pig, since the conjugate was formed in the absence of sulfate ions (25).

Conjugated morphine is also excreted by man, mainly in the form of an unidentified glucuronoside (315, 316). The glucuronic acid residue could be attached to either of the hydroxyls of the morphine molecule. Morphine addicts were found to excrete a variable quantity, averaging about 30 per cent of the injected dose, over 80 per cent of which usually appeared to be conjugated. The other 70 per cent was unaccounted for and was presumed to be oxidized or eliminated as unidentified degradation products. Orally administered morphine was conjugated to a greater extent than injected morphine and on changing from subcutaneous to oral administration there was a slight increase in the dosage required to satisfy physical dependence. On absorption from the alimentary canal the drug passes to the liver by way of the portal system before reaching the general circulation. The theory was advanced that if complete absorption is assumed, orally administered morphine may be destroyed or detoxicated by the liver before reaching the general portal system and consequently produce a decreased physiological response.

α-Isomorphine, a stereoisomer of morphine, appears to be destroyed to a greater degree in man than is morphine, since the amount of free and combined drug excreted is less in this case (316).

Oberst (317) found that heroin (3,6-diacetylmorphine) (LXX) is deacetylated to morphine which is then excreted in the free and conjugated forms by man. Morphine addicts excrete some 40 to 50 per cent of injected heroin hydrochloride as conjugated morphine and an additional 7 per cent as free morphine. A morphine addict was found to require only half as much heroin as morphine to satisfy physical dependence. When heroin and morphine were administered in doses having equal satisfying power (*i.e.*, 1:2) 7 per cent of either drug was excreted as free morphine, and about 50 per cent as conjugated morphine.

Oberst showed that codeine (3-methylmorphine) (LXXIV) is excreted by man in conjugated form (316); although in this case the phenolic hydroxyl group is methylated, the molecule still contains a free hydroxyl group. Dihydrocodeine and dihydroisocodeine, like morphine and α-isomorphine, were found to be conjugated in distinctly different proportions; hydrogenation appeared to lessen the conjugation. When both hydroxyl groups were blocked, as is the case in dihydrocodeine methyl ether (LXXV), conjugation was largely prevented and the injected drug was excreted mainly in the free state.

Penicillin (LXXVI) is reported to cause a marked increase in the excretion of glucuronic acid and the quantitative determination of glucuronic acid was suggested as a method of determining the presence and extent of absorption of penicillin (327).

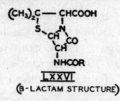

LXXVI

(β-LACTAM STRUCTURE)

No similar result following the administration of streptomycin has been reported. However, an interesting application of glucuronolactone in conjunction with streptomycin is the reported sterilization of the intestinal tract prior to surgery of the colon (337, 338). Suppression of bacterial growth, which could be maintained by streptomycin alone for not more than 4 to 6 days, was extended to 14 days or more by coadministration of glucuronolactone.

IX. *Terpenes*

It is reasonable to suppose that small amounts of terpenes are absorbed and metabolized continuously in the body, since many of them are components of essential oils and of various herbs and plants used for medicinal or culinary purposes. These products no doubt contribute to a slight extent to the normal output of glucuronic acid, although no report was found in the literature that terpene derivatives or their glucuronosides are found in the normal urine. Those members of the group that are commonly used in pharmaceutical preparations have received considerable investigation and an increase in the urinary output of glucuronic acid has been found to occur almost invariably when these compounds are administered to experimental animals.

Citronellal (LXVII) is often found with citral in lemon and rose oils and is the chief constituent of oil of citronella and oil of *Eucalyptus maculata*. When 50 g. of this terpene aldehyde was fed to rabbits, the expected open

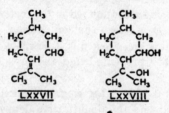

LXXVII　　　　　LXXVIII

chain oxidation product was not found in the urine, but instead 13 g. of a crystalline glucuronoside (m.p. 192°) which proved to be that of 3,8-*p*-menthanediol (LXXVIII) was isolated (210). The citronellal apparently was cyclized in the rabbit and the glucuronoside obtained was identical with that formed on feeding 3,8-*p*-menthanediol. Evidence was produced, however, to show that the cyclization of citronellal was not, strictly speaking, a biological reaction, but one which took place in the stomach under the chemical influence of gastric hydrochloric acid. Conjugation of the cyclic product is, of course, a purely biological reaction. In the conjugation product, the uronic acid residue was attached to the secondary alcohol group and the tertiary alcohol in position 8 remained free.

Cyclocitral (LXXIX) and cyclogeraniol (LXXX), when fed to rabbits, are excreted as glucuronosides (159, 161), believed in both cases to be the glucuronoside of cyclogeraniol (447).

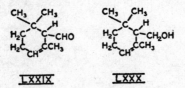

LXXIX   LXXX

a. Monocyclic Terpenes. The only hydrocarbons of the monocyclic terpene series that appear to have been investigated are *p*-menthene (142) (LXXXI) and α-phellandrene (148) (LXXXII), the latter a constituent of certain natural oils. In rabbits *p*-menthene formed a glucuronoside of unknown constitution. The formation of this conjugation product indicates that menthene is oxidized *in vivo*. When α-phellandrene was ingested by sheep, it appeared probable that the methyl group was oxidized to carboxyl and one or both of the double bonds were reduced, since phellandric acid (LXXXIII) was excreted as a conjugate with glycine (148). A glucuronoside also is formed which Wright (453) suggested was that of a *p*-menthanetriol (LXXXIV). Other products of oxidation also were formed.

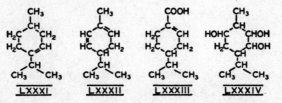

LXXXI   LXXXII   LXXXIII   LXXXIV

Hildebrandt (160) showed that carvone (LXXXV), a constituent of the oil of caraway seeds, forms a glucuronoside in the rabbit.

When fed to rabbits, 2-oxo-6,8(9)-menthadien-6-ol (LXXXVI), a keto alcohol closely related to carvone, is excreted as a conjugate with glucuronic acid but otherwise unchanged (160).

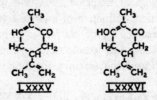

$\underline{\text{LXXXV}}$ $\underline{\text{LXXXVI}}$

d-Pulegone (LXXXVII), found in American pennyroyal oil, is converted into *d*-menthol (LXXXVIII) and *l*-pulegol (LXXXIX) when ingested by rabbits; both of the latter compounds are excreted as glucuronosides (416).

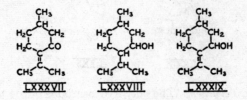

$\underline{\text{LXXXVII}}$ $\underline{\text{LXXXVIII}}$ $\underline{\text{LXXXIX}}$

Williams (447) states that reduction of the keto group is apparently the first stage in the metabolism, yielding pulegol, which then is reduced at the double bond to menthol.   Both reductions were thought to be asymmetric since two pulegols are possible and reduction of each could give two menthols.

Both Neubauer (299) and Bonanni (33) showed that *l*-menthone (XC), a product from distillation of pine wood and used as an antiseptic, germi-

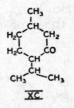

$\underline{\text{XC}}$

cide and local anesthetic, forms conjugated glucuronosides when fed to rabbits.   Hämäläinen (142) believed that menthone probably was oxidized in the rabbit, since the glucuronoside formed was converted by warm dilute sulfuric acid to a substance which he thought was 4(8)-*p*-menthen-3-one (pulegone), or one of its isomers.   Williams (444), however, showed that the carbonyl group of *l*-menthone undergoes reduction in this species with the production of *d*-neomenthol. The presence of *l*-menthol, the other possible reduction product, was not detected and therefore it was assumed that the biological reduction probably was asymmetric.

As another possible explanation Williams suggests that both *d*-neomenthol and *l*-menthol are produced, but the rate of further oxidation of *l*-menthol or its glucuronoside is greater than that of *d*-neomenthol and its glucuronoside and is such that no *l*-menthol survives *in vivo*. Some support for this second explanation is granted from the fact that when pure *d*-neomenthol was fed to rabbits 67–68 per cent was excreted as a conjugate with glucuronic acid, whereas with pure *l*-menthol only 48 per cent was excreted. When *l*-menthone was fed to rabbits, 30–40 per cent of the dose was converted to hydroxy compounds which were excreted as conjugates with glucuronic acid.

d-Isomenthone also undergoes reduction in the rabbit, since *d*-isomenthyl glucuronoside can be detected in the urine (444). The other possible reduction product, *d*-neoisomenthol, was not found. Biological reduction thus appeared to yield the opposite configuration to that produced by chemical reduction in acid solution with hydrogen and a platinum catalyst; the product here is *d*-neoisomenthol (176).

In general, it appears that monocyclic terpene alcohols are conjugated with glucuronic acid in the animal body, the glucuronic acid residue being attached to the hydroxyl group. Dihydrocarveol (XCI) is excreted as its glucuronoside by the rabbit (142). The dihydric alcohol terpin (menthane-diol) (XCII), formed in many essential oils on long standing, also formed a glucuronoside.

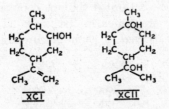

The anhydride of terpin, cineole (XCIII), is one of the chief constituents of eucalyptus and cajeput oils, and is used medicinally as an antiseptic, antispasmodic, antiperiodic and expectorant. It apparently undergoes oxidation *in vivo* to hydroxycineole, which is excreted as its glucuronoside (140). The oxidation product may be either 2- or 3-hydroxycineole (XCIV).

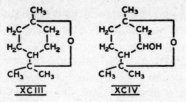

l-Menthol finds considerable use in medicine as an anesthetic and anti-septic and is a constituent of numerous common remedies. It is the chief component of oil of peppermint. None of its isomers, *d*-menthol, the *d*- and *l*-iso, -neo- and -neoisomenthols, are known to occur naturally. The *in vivo* conjugation of *l*-menthol to *l*-menthyl β-D-glucuronoside is a mechanism that has been utilized to obtain glucuronic acid, since the conjugate is easily isolated from the urine of rabbits receiving menthol; about one-half the *l*-menthol fed is excreted combined with glucuronic acid (440). In dogs only about 5 per cent of the *l*-menthol fed could be recovered in the urine as menthyl glucuronoside. Quick (339) observed that the percentage of ingested *l*-menthol that is conjugated with glucuronic acid in the rabbit depends upon the size of the dose. The larger the dose the smaller the proportion that is conjugated, showing that the rabbit has a limited capacity for conjugating menthol with glucuronic acid.

The extent to which a given dose of a menthol is conjugated with glucuronic acid also depends on the isomer fed. Williams (440) has shown that menthols of the dextro configuration are excreted as glucuronosides to a greater extent than the *l*-menthols. This behavior has been used by Williams (441, 442) for the optical resolution of *dl*-menthol and *dl*-isomenthol.

b. Bicyclic Terpenes. Saturated thujane compounds appear to be degraded to monocyclic structures in the body. Thujyl alcohol (XCV), found in oil of absinthe, is excreted as the glucuronosides of 2,4-*p*-menthane-

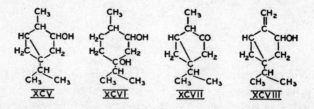

diol (XCVI) and thujyl alcohol, when fed to rabbits (142). Thujone (XCVII) behaved similarly, forming a glucuronoside believed to be that of 2,4-*p*-menthanediol. When the thujane structure contained an unsaturated bond, however, the bicyclic structure tended to survive. Sabinol (XCVIII) when fed to animals yielded sabinyl glucuronoside (m.p. 82–83°) (141, 142).

Whether the α- and β-pinenes (XCIX and C) are converted into monocyclic structures *in vivo* is not known. Hämäläinen (142) has shown that both compounds are converted to glucuronic acid conjugates of undetermined nature in the rabbit. These conjugates yielded the aromatic hydrocarbon cymene (CI) on heating with dilute acids.

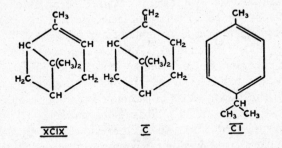

Rimini (364) reported that carone (CII) is oxidized in the dog to 4-hydroxycarone (CIII), which is conjugated with glucuronic acid and excreted.

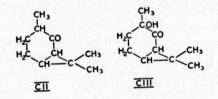

Ingested camphane (CIV) is oxidized to a mixture of *d*- and *l*-borneols (CV) and excreted as the corresponding glucuronosides (142).

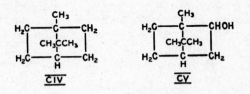

d-Borneol is the main constituent of Borneo camphor and its metabolism in the animal body appears fairly straightforward. In man it is almost entirely eliminated as bornyl glucuronoside, 80 per cent of a 2-g. dose being thus excreted in 10 hrs. (336). The dog excretes 52 per cent as the glucuronoside (346). According to Magnus-Levy (227) *d*- and *l*-borneol are equally conjugated in dogs and rabbits, but the work of Pryde and Williams (334) suggests that *d*-borneol is excreted as a glucuronoside by the dog to a greater extent than is the *l*-isomer. Hämäläinen (144) found that normal rabbits excreted 86 per cent of ingested *d*-bornyl acetate, 92 per cent of *l*-bornyl acetate and 95 per cent of *dl*-borneol as the glucuronosides. Glucuronosides of the borneols and isoborneols form crystalline zinc salts which are easily isolated because of their insolubility in water (139). This behavior has been used to advantage in obtaining glucuronic acid for experimental purposes; borneol is fed to animals, particularly dogs, and the resulting bornyl glucuronoside is isolated from the urine.

Ordinary camphor (*d*-camphor) (CVI) has been used to a considerable extent as a temporary cardiac stimulant and its fate in the animal body has been investigated extensively. In 1879 Schmiedeberg and Meyer (381) isolated three metabolites of camphor from dog urine, "α-camphoglycuronic acid" ($[\alpha]_D$ −32.85°), "β-camphoglycuronic acid" and a nitrogenous compound that they called "uramido-camphoglycuronic acid." The α-compound was obtained in the largest amount and all three yielded hydroxycamphor on hydrolysis. These investigators used common or *dextro*-camphor and later work has shown that the behavior of *dl*- and *l*-camphor in the body is similar to that of the *dextro* isomer. Not until

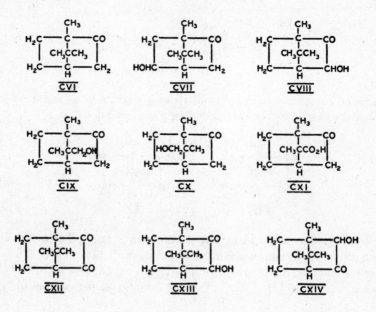

nearly 50 years later was there any definite information regarding the constitution of the hydroxycamphors. Then Asahina and Ishidate (7–10) showed that the α-camphoglycuronic acid of Schmiedeberg and Meyer contained two hydroxycamphors which they identified as 3- and 5-hydroxycamphors (CVII and CVIII). They also demonstrated that α- and β-camphoglycuronic acid differed only in the proportion of the 3- and 5-hydroxycamphors which they contained. Further investigations in which very large amounts of biosynthetic hydroxycamphors were worked up showed that other metabolic products were present in small amounts. These were *cis*- and *trans*-π-hydroxycamphors (CIX and CX) and *trans*-π-apocamphor-7-carboxylic acid (CXI). The main oxidation product of camphor was 5-hydroxycamphor but appreciable amounts of the 3-hydroxy derivative were formed.

When camphorquinone (CXII) is fed to dogs, glucuronosides are excreted that can be hydrolyzed to 3-hydroxycamphor (CXIII) and 2-hydroxyepicamphor (CXIV) (362). Thus, it appeared that either keto group may be reduced but that both probably cannot be reduced simultaneously.

Reinartz *et al.* (361) reported that 5-oxocamphor (CXV) was in part reduced in the 5-position to the endo form but that oxidation occurred in the 4- and π-position to form the corresponding hydroxydiketocamphanes. An acid, $C_{10}H_{12}O_3$, which they believed to be cyclocamphanone-π-carboxylic acid (CXVI) also was formed. Formation of the latter compound was surprising, since it involves reduction at C_5 followed by dehydration at C_3 and C_5 and simultaneous oxidation at $C\pi$. Ishidate, Kawahata and Nakazawa (181) reinvestigated the metabolism of the 5-oxocamphor and were unable to confirm the results of Reinartz *et al.* When they fed *d*-5-oxocamphor to dogs and hydrolyzed the resulting excreted glucuronosides, the only compound obtained was *d*-5-hydroxycamphor (CXVII), formation of which involves the reduction of one keto group.

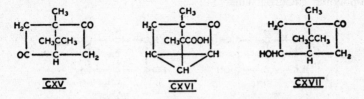

The hydrocarbon camphene (CXVIII) is of interest because, in the rabbit, it forms a glycol which is excreted as the monoglucuronoside; the latter was isolated as a levorotatory potassium salt (111). It was not known at which hydroxyl group the glucuronic acid was attached.

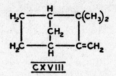

CXVIII

Camphenilol (CXIX) is conjugated without change by the rabbit and excreted as the glucuronoside (m.p. 150-3°) (142). The corresponding camphor, camphenilone, behaves unlike most ketones of the bicyclic terpene group, since its keto group is reduced to a secondary alcohol group. The inactive form was fed by Hämäläinen (142) and a mixture of d- and l-camphenilols was produced. The glucuronosides excreted contained more d- than l-camphenilol.

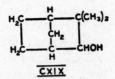

CXIX

Isobornyl glucuronoside was the principle product excreted by the rabbit after administration of racemic isoborneol (CXX) (139).

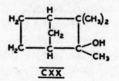

CXX

The fenchane structure appears to be stable *in vivo*. Both l-fenchyl (CXXI) and l-isofenchyl (CXXII) alcohols are excreted by rabbits as the corresponding glucuronosides (142).

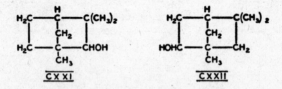

CXXI   CXXII

The fate of d-fenchone (CXXIII), a camphor of this group that occurs in fennel oil, was studied by Rimini (363, 364) and by Reinartz and Zanke (360). Rimini showed that in the dog fenchone probably was oxidized to a hydroxyfenchone. Reinartz and Zanke reported that, in addition to Rimini's ketone which they proved to be 4-hydroxyfenchone (CXXIV), other products were formed. From the urine of dogs receiving *d*-fenchone they separated the glucuronosides as lead salts. After removing the lead with sulfuric acid, the resulting solution was hydrolyzed and a mixture of hydroxyfenchones resulted in which the presence of 4- and 5-hydroxyfenchones (CXXIV and CXXV) and π-hydroxyfenchone (CXXVI) was demonstrated. The hydrolyzate as such could not be separated into its constituents, but upon oxidation with CrO_3 and $KMnO_4$ it yielded unchanged 4-hydroxyfenchone while the 5-hydroxy derivative was recovered as 5-ketofenchone. A carboxylic acid, apparently formed from π-hydroxyfenchone, was identified by the fact that on heating above its melting point it was decarboxylated to fenchosantenone (CXXVII).

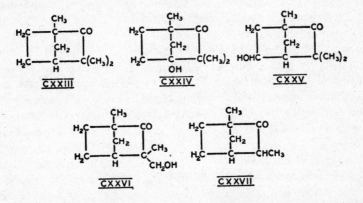

β-Santenol (CXXVIII) (inactive) is converted to its glucuronoside in the rabbit (142). α-Santenol (CXXIX) (inactive) behaved similarly. The corresponding ketone, α-santenone or π-norcamphor, seemed to be metabolized in a manner similar to camphor, for the keto group remained and oxidation occurred elsewhere in the molecule, the glucuronoside of α-santenonol being excreted. The location of the hydroxyl group in this biosynthetic α-santenonol was, however, uncertain.

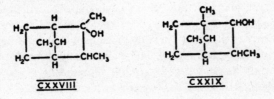

When Chosen ginseng extract was fed to rabbits the urinary output of glucuronic acid was increased in proportion to the dose of the ginseng (321). It was thought that the sesquiterpene of the ginseng probably was decomposed in the body and conjugated with glucuronic acid.

X. *Organic Compounds of Arsenic*

Several organic compounds of arsenic are used in the treatment of protozoal infection. These drugs are characterized by a relatively low toxicity as compared to inorganic arsenic compounds. Information regarding their fate in the animal body is still incomplete and explanation of their therapeutic action is difficult without such knowledge. These compounds are inactive against parasites *in vitro*, and *in vivo* they show a latent period during which there is no evidence of parasiticidal action. This latent period is followed by a gradual destruction of the parasites, indicating that the active chemotherapeutic agents are metabolites of the drugs rather than the drugs themselves.

Sieberg (394) found that 4,4'-arsenobenzoic acid (CXXX), when injected subcutaneously into a calf, is considerably degraded, a large amount of benzoic acid being produced. The arseno linkage was split and the trivalent arsenic was oxidized to the pentavalent form, for *p*-carboxyphenylarsonic acid (CXXXI) could be isolated from the urine. He believed that the arsonic acid was conjugated with glycine. Following arsenobenzoic acid injections, however, the urine was strongly reducing and was shown to contain glucuronic acid. Contrary to Sieberg's suggestion that the glucuronic acid excreted is in the free state, Williams (447) considers it probable that it is combined as a reducing ester glucuronoside of benzoic acid or possibly of *p*-carboxyphenylarsonic acid.

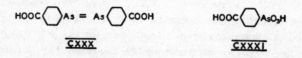

XI. *Sex Hormones*

The sex hormones are representatives of a group of compounds derived from the cyclopentanophenanthrene nucleus, many of which are known to possess intense physiological activity. Type of activity varies widely with different members of the group, in spite of the fact that their basic structure is the same. Besides the sex hormones themselves, the group includes other sterols such as cholesterol, vitamin D, the bile acids, some of the cardiac stimulants and a number of hydrocarbons that have been shown to possess carcinogenic activity. Physiological responses similar to those produced by various members of the steroid group are shown also by certain compounds which do not possess this basic structure; examples of such compounds are the synthetic estrogens.

Metabolism of the steroids as a class has not been studied from the standpoint of a possible connection with glucuronic acid, but a number of observations have been made that suggest that glucuronic acid may play a role of real importance and that intensive investigation in this field might prove fruitful.

Stilbestrol (CXXXII), hexestrol (CXXXIII) and dienestrol (a 3,4-di(p-hydroxyphenyl)hexa-2,4-diene (CXXXIV)) have been shown to possess therapeutic value both as synthetic estrogens (83) and as anticancer compounds (136). Stroud (410) showed that all three of these compounds, on injection into rabbits, were excreted in a combined form. Mazur and Shorr (252) isolated stilbestrol from the urine of rabbits as the monoglucuronoside. Dodgson *et al.* (84), by measuring the elevation of urinary glucuronosides, found that 70 per cent of injected stilbestrol was excreted by rabbits as the glucuronoside. Similar results were obtained with hexestrol, and indications were that dienestrol behaved similarly; in the latter case the stability of the glucuronoside linkage prevented accurate estimation of the uronic acid by the method used. All three glucuronosides were obtained in crystalline form and had the following properties:

Compound	Formula	m.p.	$[a]_D^{20}$
Stilbestrol monoglucuronoside dihydrate	$C_{24}H_{28}O_8 \cdot 2H_2O$	179° (decomp.)	−56.5° (in ethanol)
Hexestrol monoglucuronoside trihydrate	$C_{24}H_{30}O_8 \cdot 3H_2O$	183°–184° (decomp.)	−66.3° (in 0.1 N NaOH)
Dienestrol monoglucuronoside monohydrate	$C_{24}H_{26}O_8 \cdot H_2O$	181°–183° (decomp.)	−45.9° (in 0.1 N NaOH)

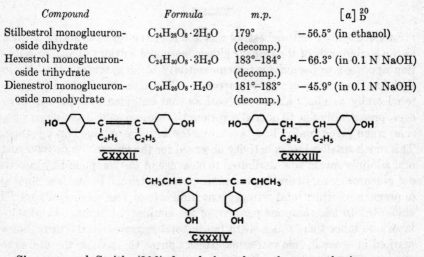

Simpson and Smith (396) found that these three synthetic estrogens (stilbestrol, hexestrol and dienestrol) when administered to rabbits and man were excreted as monoglucuronosides to a much greater extent than as free estrogens or ethereal sulfates.

These glucuronosides are reported (395) to have only 5 to 10 per cent of the activity of the corresponding free estrogens. The reason for this lowered activity was not known, but it was suggested that it might be the result of an intrinsically lower estrogenic potency, of the liberation of only a small portion of estrogen, or of more rapid elimination from the organism. The amount of free estrogen liberated, if any, appeared to be insufficient to account for even the slight biological activity shown.

The natural estrogen estriol (CXXXV) also occurs conjugated with glucuronic acid (237). Such a conjugate, known as emmenin, is obtained from the human placenta. A glucuronoside of estriol also was isolated from human pregnancy urine, and a crystalline sodium salt was prepared. The glucuronic acid was thought to be attached by a glycosidic linkage to the hydroxyl at either position 16 or 17 of the steroid nucleus. Estriol appeared to be conjugated with sulfuric rather than glucuronic acid in the urine of pregnant mares.

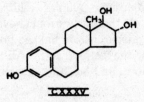

CXXXV

Subcutaneously injected estriol was about thirty times as active in mice as the sodium salt of the urinary glucuronoside of estriol. Thus, conjugation appeared to decrease estrogenic activity to an extent comparable to that found with the synthetic estrogens. The activity of estriol administered orally was only about one-tenth of that obtained by injection, however, presumably due to poor absorption; the sodium salt of the glucuronoside, when given orally, had two-thirds the activity obtained on injection. This much smaller loss in activity observed for the glucuronoside following oral administration was attributed to cleavage of the compound by intestinal glucuronidase, liberating the more potent estriol. In the last months of pregnancy, when total estrogen excretion is high, free estrone and estriol amounted to less than one per cent of the conjugated forms. In pseudolabor and labor there was a slight fall in total estrogens in the urine but a marked increase in free estrogens, which appear to sensitize the uterus to the oxytocic substances, causing uterine contraction and parturition.

Shapiro (392) reported that heat could be produced in castrated mice by subcutaneous injection of estradiol glucuronoside. He also found that the glucuronoside of dehydroandrosterone caused a slight increase in comb growth of capons when applied locally.

Other steroid hormones excreted under certain conditions in conjugation with glucuronic acid are pregnanediol, (pregnane-3)(α),20(α)-diol, (CXXXVI) (427) and a number of closely related compounds including pregnane-3(α)-ol-20-one (238); pregnane-3(α),17,20-triol (248); pregnane-3(α),20(α)-diol (248), and pregnane-3-(α),17-diol-20-one (249). Pregnanediol glucuronoside is excreted in increasing amounts not only throughout pregnancy, but also appears in normal urine during the luteal phase of the menstrual cycle.

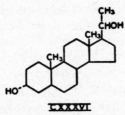

CXXXVI

Brooksbank and Haslewood (47), applying a recently described entrainment method for estimation of sodium pregnanediol glucuronosidate to normal human male urine, obtained results indicating that other glucuronosides of similar solubility were being determined simultaneously. By separating the products and hydrolyzing, they were able to identify Δ16-androsten-3(α)-ol.

Buehler, Katzman, Doisy and Doisy (49) used a glucuronidase preparation to liberate urinary steroids from their conjugates. In almost all cases higher values for free steroids were obtained than by the usual method— employing hydrochloric acid for hydrolysis. The difference was attributed to the destructive action of the acid. What was pointed out as surprising was the fact that so large an amount of estrogen in human pregnancy urine and of ketosteroids in normal human urine appeared to be conjugated with glucuronic acid.

The relation between the β-glucuronidase content of animal tissues and injected "glucuronogenic" substances is obscure, particularly in view of the evidence that this enzyme is not responsible for glucuronic acid conjugation (197). As mentioned earlier (p. 33), this recent work suggests the need for a re-interpretation of some of the data reported by Fishman. Although he found no increase in β-glucuronidase activity of the sex organs of dogs and mice that had been fed borneol and menthol, when the "natural" estrogenic hormones, estriol, sodium estriol glucuronosidate, estrone, and also the synthetic estrogen stilbestrol were injected into ovariectomized mice, the uterine β-glucuronidase activity was raised 100 per cent or more above the level in the control group (101, 104); in some cases the enzyme activity of the vagina was also increased. However, the β-glucuronidase activity of the liver, kidney, spleen, blood cells and plasma remained largely unchanged. Non-estrogens such as progesterone, pregnanediol, borneol and menthol, did not effect the uterine β-glucuronidase activity. Fishman (101) advances the hypothesis that the physiological significance of the enzyme is the synthesis of the glucuronoside of the hormone as the initial step in the utilization of the complex by the tissue. As pregnancy proceeded, excretion of the glucuronosides of estriol and pregnanediol became progressively greater, possibly functioning to protect the fetus and the maternal body from the deleterious effects of large quantities of the estrogen. Fishman believed that, unlike most other ingested drugs, both the natural and synthetic estrogens are conjugated, not in the liver, but in the uterus, the site of their activity. This phenomenon was not explained but it was suggested that glucuronidase has a fundamental role in the physiological action of the estrogenic hormones.

Carcinomas of the breast and gastrointestinal tract were reported by Fishman (102) to contain more β-glucuronidase than did corresponding, uninvolved tissue. Further observations on cancerous tissue from other organs, together with the finding of enhanced β-glucuronidase activity of lymph nodes involved by cancer, led Fishman and Anlyan (103) to take the view that elevated β-glucuronidase is probably a characteristic of malignant cells, although a high glucuronidase activity in a tissue does not necessarily imply malignant change. Karunairatnam, Kerr and Levvy (197) reported that glucuronidase activity in mouse tumors was higher than in normal adult tissue and they related glucuronidase activity to the degree of cell proliferation in progress. In accordance with their evidence that β-glucuronidase is distinct from the enzyme system responsible for glucuronic acid conjugation, they suggested that the two enzyme systems, taken together, may provide a method for regulating the transport, action and excretion of physiologically active glucuronogenic compounds. An alternate suggestion was that their function may be to provide free glucuronic acid or a transformation product for building into more complex molecules.

The significance of the higher glucuronidase activities in tumor tissues is unknown. There is, for example, an increased enzyme activity of pregnant cervix (at term), in some cases giving values overlapping those obtained from the malignant tissue (318). However, the difference between the enzyme activity of normal and malignant tissue is sufficiently pronounced that its measurement has been found to be a diagnostic aid in female genital carcinoma, particularly that of the lower genital tract.

Anlyan, Gamble and Hoster (6) reported values for β-glucuronidase activities in blood plasma and buffy coat of normal patients and of patients with various diseases. Values were particularly high in acute myelogenous leukemia and in the terminal phase of chronic myelogenous leukemia.

BIBLIOGRAPHY

1. Abel, J. J., and Rowntree, L. G. *J. Pharmacol.* **1**, 231 (1909).
2. Adler, O. *Arch. exptl. Path. Pharmakol.* **58**, 167 (1907).
3. Almquist, H. J., Mecchi, E., Stokstad, E. L. R., and Manning, P. D. V. *J. Biol. Chem.* **134**, 465 (1940).
4. Almquist, H. J., Stokstad, E. L. R., Mecchi, E., and Manning, P. D. V. *J. Biol. Chem.* **134**, 213 (1940).
5. Ambrose, A. M., Power, F. W., and Sherwin, C. P. *J. Biol. Chem.* **101**, 669 (1933).
6. Anlyan, A. J., Gamble, J., and Hoster, H. A. *Cancer* **3**, 116 (1950).
7. Asahina, Y., and Ishidate, M. *Ber.* **61B**, 533 (1928).
8. Asahina, Y., and Ishidate, M. *Ber.* **66B**, 1673 (1933).
9. Asahina, Y., and Ishidate, M. *Ber.* **67B**, 71 (1934).
10. Asahina, Y., and Ishidate, M. *Ber.* **68B**, 947 (1935).
11. Atkinson, A. J. *J. Am. Med. Assoc.* **98**, 1153 (1932).
12. Avery, O. T., Heidelberger, M., and Goebel, W. F. *J. Exptl. Med.* **42**, 709 (1925).
13. Baeyer, A. *Ann.* **155**, 257 (1870).
14. Baier, W. E., Bryant, E. F., Joseph, G. H., and Palmer, G. H. *Science* **101**, 670 (1945).
15. Baldoni, A. *Jahresber. Tierchem.* **35**, 125 (1905).
16. Baumann, E. *Z. physiol. Chem.* **1**, 60 (1877).
17. Baumann, E. *Z. physiol. Chem.* **8**, 190 (1883).
18. Baumann, E., and Preusse, C. *Z. physiol. Chem.* **3**, 156 (1879).
19. Baumgarten, O. *Z. exptl. Path. Therap.* **2**, 53 (1905–1906).
20. Becker, B., and Friedenwald, J. S. *Arch. Biochem.* **22**, 101 (1949).
21. Benham, G. H. *Can. J. Research* **23E**, 71 (1945).
22. Berenblum, I., Crowfoot, D., Holiday, E. R., and Schoental, R. *Cancer Research* **3**, 151 (1943).
23. Bergell, P., and Pschorr, R. *Z. physiol. Chem.* **38**, 16 (1903).
24. Bergmann, F. *Biochem. Z.* **267**, 296 (1933).
25. Bernheim, F., and Bernheim, M. L. C. *J. Pharmacol.* **83**, 85 (1945).
26. Bertagnini, C. *Ann.* **97**, 248 (1856).
27. Bial, M. *Deut. med. Wochschr.* **28**, 253 (1902).
28. Biberfeld, J. *Biochem. Z.* **65**, 479 (1914).
29. Bird, H. R., Oleson, J. J., Elvehjem, C. A., and Hart, E. B. *J. Biol. Chem.* **126**, 671 (1938).
30. Blix, G., and Snellman, O. *Nature* **153**, 587 (1944).
31. Blum, F. *Z. physiol. Chem.* **16**, 514 (1892).
32. Boku, S., and Kin, T. *J. Chosen Med. Assoc.* **21**, 67 (1931).
33. Bonanni, A. *Arch. farmacol. sper.* **1**, 469, 498 (1902).
34. Borgström, B. *Acta Med. Scand.* **133**, 7 (1949); *Chem. Abstracts* **43**, 6300 (1949).

35. Bourne, M. C., and Young, L.   *Biochem. J.* **28**, 803 (1934).
36. Boyd, W. C.   Fundamentals of Immunology.   2nd ed., Interscience, New York, 1947, p. 126.
37. Boyland, E., and Levi, A. A.   *Biochem. J.* **29**, 2679 (1935).
38. Boyland, E., and Levi, A. A.   *Biochem. J.* **30**, 728 (1936).
39. Brahm, C.   *Z. physiol. Chem.* **28**, 439 (1899).
40. Braunstein, A. E., and Parschin, A. N.   *Biochem. Z.* **235**, 344 (1931).
41. Braunstein, A. E., Parschin, A. N., and Chalisowa, O. D.   *Biochem. Z.* **235**, 311 (1931).
42. Bray, H. G., Gregory, J. E., and Stacey, M.   *Biochem. J.* **38**, 142 (1944).
43. Bray, H. G., Humphris, B. G., and Thorpe, W. V.   *Biochem. J.* **45**, 241 (1949).
44. Bray, H. G., Ryman, B. E., and Thorpe, W. V.   *Biochem. J.* **41**, 212 (1947).
45. Bray, H. G., Ryman, B. E., and Thorpe, W. V.   *Biochem. J.* **43**, 561 (1948).
46. Bray, H. G., Thorpe, W. V., and Wood, P. B.   *Biochem. J.* **45**, 45 (1949).
47. Brooksbank, B. W. L., and Haslewood, G. A. D.   *Biochem. J.* **44**, Suppl., p. iii (1949).
48. Bryant, E. F., Palmer, G. H., and Joseph, G. H.   *Ind. Eng. Chem., Anal. Ed.* **16**, 74 (1944).
49. Buehler, H. J., Katzman, P. A., Doisy, P. P., and Doisy, E. A.   *Proc. Exptl. Biol. Med.* **72**, 297 (1949).
50. Burkhart, B., Baur, L., and Link, K. P.   *J. Biol. Chem.* **104**, 171 (1934).
51. Chain, E., and Duthie, E. S.   *Brit. J. Exptl. Path.* **21**, 324 (1940).
52. Chalmers, J. G., and Crowfoot, D.   *Biochem. J.* **35**, 1270 (1941).
53. Channon, H. J., Mills, G. T., and Williams, R. T.   *Biochem. J.* **38**, 70 (1944).
54. Cohen, S. S.   *J. Biol. Chem.* **144**, 353 (1942).
55. Cohn, R.   *Z. physiol. Chem.* **18**, 112 (1894).
56. Coombs, H. I., and Hele, T. S.   *Biochem. J.* **21**, 611 (1927).
57. Crandall, L. A.   U. S. Patent 1,950,100, March 6, 1934.
58. Crandall, L. A., Chesley, F. F., Gray, R. E., and Robinson, H. E.   *J. Nutrition* **17**, 53 (1939).
59. Crandall, L. A., and Roberts, G. M.   *Proc. Soc. Exptl. Biol. Med.* **30**, 704 (1933).
60. Crandall, L. A., Roberts, G. M., and Gibbs, J. W.   *Proc. Soc. Exptl. Biol. Med.* **29**, 1082 (1932).
61. Crandall, L. A., Roberts, G. M., and Snorf, L. D.   *Am. J. Digestive Diseases Nutrition* **3**, 289 (1936).
62. Crépy, O.   *Arch. sci. physiol.* **1**, 427 (1947).
63. Csonka, F. A.   *J. Biol. Chem.* **60**, 545 (1924).
64. Dakin, H. D.   *J. Biol. Chem.* **5**, 173 (1908).
65. Dakin, H. D.   *J. Biol. Chem.* **6**, 221 (1909).
66. Dakin, H. D.   *J. Biol. Chem.* **7**, 103 (1909–1910).
67. Dakin, H. D.   *J. Biol. Chem.* **8**, 11 (1910).
68. Dean, G. R., private communication.
69. Deichmann, W. B.   *J. Lab. Clin. Med.* **28**, 770 (1943).
70. Deichmann, W. B.   *Proc. Soc. Exptl. Biol. Med.* **54**, 335 (1943).
71. Deichmann, W. B.   *Arch. Biochem.* **3**, 345 (1944).
72. Deichmann, W. B., and Dierker, M.   *J. Biol. Chem.* **163**, 753 (1946).
73. Deichmann, W. B., and Thomas, G.   *J. Ind. Hyg. Toxicol.* **25**, 286 (1943).
74. Deichmann, W. B., and Wetherup, S.   *Arch. Biochem.* **7**, 401 (1945).

75. De Meio, R. H., and Arnolt, R. I. *J. Biol. Chem.* **156**, 577 (1944).
76. Dickson, A. D., Otterson, H., and Link, K. P. *J. Am. Chem. Soc.* **52**, 775 (1930).
77. Dische, Z. *Biochem. Z.* **189**, 77 (1927).
78. Dische, Z. *J. Biol. Chem.* **167**, 189 (1947).
79. Dische, Z. *J. Biol. Chem.* **171**, 725 (1947).
80. Di Somma, A. A. *J. Biol. Chem.* **133**, 277 (1940).
81. Dobriner, K., Hofmann, K., and Rhoads, C. P. *Science* **93**, 600 (1941).
82. Dobson, F., and Williams, R. T. *Biochem. J.* **40**, 215 (1946).
83. Dodds, E. C. *Vitamins and Hormones* **3**, 229 (1945).
84. Dodgson, K. S., Garton, G. A., Stubbs, A. L., and Williams, R. T. *Biochem. J.* **42**, 357 (1948).
85. Dodgson, K. S., Garton, G. A., and Williams, R. T. *Biochem. J.* **41**, Proc. 1 (1947).
86. Dodgson, K. S., and Williams, R. T. *Biochem. J.* **45**, 381 (1949).
87. Donath, J. *Ber.* **14**, 1769 (1881).
88. Drummond, J. C., and Finar, I. L. *Biochem. J.* **32**, 79 (1938).
89. Dziewiatkowski, D. D., and Lewis, H. B. *J. Biol. Chem.* **153**, 49 (1944).
90. Egami, H. *J. Chem. Soc. Japan* **62**, 277 (1941); *Chem. Abstracts* **36**, 6948 (1942).
91. Ehrlich, F., and Rehorst, K. *Ber.* **62B**, 628 (1929).
92. Ehrlich, F., and Schubert, F. *Ber.* **62B**, 1974 (1929).
93. Elson, L. A., Goulden, F., and Warren, F. L. *Biochem. J.* **39**, 301 (1945).
94. Elson, L. A., and Warren, F. L. *Biochem. J.* **38**, 217 (1944).
95. Endoh, C. *Biochem. Z.* **152**, 276 (1924).
96. Enklewitz, E., and Lasker, M. *J. Biol. Chem.* **110**, 443 (1935).
97. v. Fenyvessy, B. *Z. physiol. Chem.* **30**, 552 (1900).
98. v. Fenyvessy, B. *Arch. intern. pharmacodynamie* **12**, 407 (1904).
99. Fischer, E., and Piloty, O. *Ber.* **24**, 521 (1891).
100. Fishman, W. H. *J. Biol. Chem.* **136**, 229 (1940).
101. Fishman, W. H. *J. Biol. Chem.* **169**, 7 (1947).
102. Fishman, W. H. *Science* **105**, 646 (1947).
103. Fishman, W. H., and Anlyan, A. J. *Science* **106**, 66 (1947).
104. Fishman, W. H., and Fishman, L. W. *J. Biol. Chem.* **152**, 487 (1944).
105. Flaschenträger, B., Cagianut, B., and Meier, F. *Helv. Chim. Acta* **28**, 1489 (1945).
106. Flatow, L. *Z. physiol. Chem.* **64**, 367 (1910).
107. Fleig, C. *J. pharm. chim.*, 6e serie **29**, 55 (1909).
108. Florkin, M. *Compt. rend. soc. biol.* **126**, 916 (1937).
109. Fogelson, S. M. *J. Am. Med. Assoc.* **96**, 673 (1931).
110. Follett, A. E. *J. Biol. Chem.* **176**, 177 (1948).
111. Fromm, E., Hildebrandt, H., and Clemens, P. *Z. physiol. Chem.* **37**, 189 (1902–1903).
112. Fühner, H. *Arch. exptl. Path. Pharmakol.* **55**, 27 (1906).
113. Galimard, J. E. *Bull. soc. chim. biol.* **26**, 185 (1944).
114. Garton, G. A., and Williams, R. T. *Biochem. J.* **43**, 206 (1948).
115. Garton, G. A., and Williams, R. T. *Biochem. J.* **44**, 234 (1949).
116. Garton, G. A., and Williams, R. T. *Biochem. J.* **45**, 158 (1949).
117. Georgescu, J. *Ann. physiol. physicochim. biol.* **8**, 122 (1932).
118. Gibbs, J. W., and Crandall, L. A., unpublished, reported in (61).
119. Giemsa, G. *Ber.* **33B**, 2996 (1900).

120. Gilligan, D. R., and Beck, E. M.   *J. Clin. Investigation* **24**, 301 (1945).
121. Goebel, W. F.   *J. Exptl. Med.* **64**, 29 (1936).
122. Goebel, W. F.   *J. Biol. Chem.* **122**, 649 (1938).
123. Goebel, W. F.   *J. Exptl. Med.* **68**, 469 (1938).
124. Goebel, W. F.   *J. Exptl. Med.* **69**, 353 (1939).
125. Goebel, W. F.   *Nature* **143**, 77 (1939).
126. Goebel, W. F.   *J. Exptl. Med.* **72**, 33 (1940).
127. Goebel, W. F., and Avery, O. T.   *J. Exptl. Med.* **50**, 521, 533 (1929).
128. Goebel, W. F., and Babers, F. H.   *J.'Biol. Chem.* **100**, 573 (1933).
129. Goebel, W. F., Babers, F. H., and Avery, O. T.   *J. Exptl. Med.* **60**, 85 (1934).
130. Goebel, W. F., and Hotchkiss, R. D.   *J. Exptl. Med.* **66**, 191 (1937).
131. Goldberg, S. A.   *Am. J. Clin. Path.* **14**, 1'(1944).
132. Goldschmiedt, G.   *Z. physiol. Chem.* **65**, 389 (1910); **67**, 194 (1910).
133. Gross, E. G., and Thompson, V.   *J. Pharmacol.* **68**, 413 (1940).
134. Guerbet, M., and Mayer, A.   *Ann. physiol. physicochim. biol.* **8**, 117 (1932).
135. Guerrero, A. H., and Williams, R. T.   *Nature* **161**, 930 (1948).
136. Haddow, A.   *Brit. Med. Bull.* **4**, 417 (1947).
137. Hadidian, Z., and Pirie, N. W.   *Biochem. J.* **42**, 260 (1948).
138. Halberkann, J., and Fretwurst, F.   *Arquiv. inst. biol. (São Paulo)* **11**, 149 (1940);
     Chem. Abstracts **36**, 101 (1942).
139. Hämäläinen, J.   *Skand. Arch. Physiol.* **23**, 86 (1910).
140. Hämäläinen, J.   *Skand. Arch. Physiol.* **24**, 1 (1911).
141. Hämäläinen, J.   *Biochem. Z.* **41**, 241 (1912).
142. Hämäläinen, J.   *Skand. Arch. Physiol.* **27**, 141 (1912).
143. Hämäläinen, J.   *Skand. Arch. Physiol.* **30**, 187 (1913).
144. Hämäläinen, J., and Sjöström, S.   *Skand. Arch. Physiol.* **24**, 113 (1911).
145. Hanson, S. W. F., Mills, G. T., and Williams, R. T.   *Biochem. J.* **38**, 274 (1944).
146. Hardegger, E., and Spitz, D.   *Helv. Chim. Acta* **32**, 2165 (1949); **33**, 337 (1950).
147. Hartles, R. L., and Williams, R. T.   *Biochem. J.* **43**, 296 (1948).
148. Harvey, J. M., White, M., and Jones, T. G. H.   *Univ. Queensland Papers, Dept.
     Chem.* **1**, No. 23 (1942); cited by Williams (447).
149. Haworth, W. N.   *Proc. Roy. Soc. London* **A186**, 1 (1946).
150. Heffter, A.   *Arch. exptl. Path. Pharmakol.* **35**, 342 (1895).
151. Hegsted, D. M., Hier, S. W., Elvehjem, C. A., and Hart, E. B.   *J. Biol. Chem.*
     139, 863 (1941).
152. Heidelberger, M., and Hobby, G. L.   *Proc. Natl. Acad. Sci.* **28**, 516 (1942).
153. Heidelberger, M., Kabat, E. A., and Mayer, M.   *J. Exptl. Med.* **75**, 35 (1942).
154. Heidelberger, M., Kendall, F. E., and Scherp, H. W.   *J. Exptl. Med.* **64**, 559
     (1936).
155. Hemingway, A., Pryde, J., and Williams, R. T.   *Biochem. J.* **28**, 136 (1934).
156. Hepburn, J. S., and Lazarchick, M.   *Am. J. Pharm.* **102**, 560 (1930).
157. Hermanns, L.   *Z. physiol. Chem.* **85**, 233 (1913).
158. Hesselvik, L.   *Acta Med. Scand.* **105**, 153 (1940).
159. Hildebrandt, H.   *Arch. exptl. Path. Pharmakol.* **46**, 261 (1901).
160. Hildebrandt, H.   *Z. physiol. Chem.* **36**, 441, 452 (1902).
161. Hildebrandt, H.   *Beitr. chem. Physiol. Path.* **4**, 251 (1904).
162. Hildebrandt, H.   *Beitr. chem. Physiol. Path.* **7**, 433 (1905–1906).
163. Hildebrandt, H.   *Beitr. chem. Physiol. Path.* **7**, 438 (1905–1906).

164. Hildebrandt, H. *Beitr. chem. Physiol. Path.* **9**, 472 (1907).
165. Hildebrandt, H. *Biochem. Z.* **21**, 1 (1909).
166. Hinsberg, O., and Kast, A. *Zentr. med. Wiss.* **25**, 145 (1887); cited by Williams (447).
167. Hirsch, C. *Acta Chir. Scand.* **90**, *Suppl.* 83 (1944).
168. His, W. *Arch. exptl. Path. Pharmakol.* **22**, 253 (1887).
169. Hodas, J. H., Brandon, H., and Maloney, J. F. *J. Lancet* **69**, 385 (1949).
170. Holmgren, H., and Wilander, O. *Z. mikroskop. anat. Forsch.* **42**, 242 (1937); *Chem. Abstracts* **32**, 7978 (1938).
171. Horn, F. *Z. physiol. Chem.* **238**, 84 (1936).
172. Horn, F. *Z. physiol. Chem.* **242**, 23 (1936).
173. Horn, F. *Z. physiol. Chem.* **249**, 82 (1937).
174. Hotchkiss, R. D., and Goebel, W. F. *J. Biol. Chem.* **121**, 195 (1937).
175. Houet, R., Duchateau, G., and Florkin, M. *Compt. rend. soc. biol.* **135**, 412 (1941).
176. Hückel, W., and Niggemeyer, H. *Ber.* **72B**, 1354 (1939).
177. Huebner, C. F., and Link, K. P., Abstracts of Papers, 110th Meeting American Chemical Society, Chicago, Ill., Sept. 9–13, 1946, p. 5R.
178. Humphrey, J. H. *Biochem. J.* **40**, 435 (1946).
179. Ichihara, K., and Tamura, S. *Z. physiol. Chem.* **214**, 33 (1933).
180. Inagaki, S. *Z. physiol. Chem.* **214**, 25 (1933).
181. Ishidate, M., Kawahata, H., and Nakazawa, K. *Ber.* **74B**, 1707 (1941).
182. Jaffe, M. *Ber.* **7**, 1673 (1874).
183. Jaffe, M. *Z. physiol. Chem.* **2**, 47 (1878–1879).
184. Jaffe, M. *Ber.* **34**, 2737 (1901).
185. Jaffe, M. *Ber.* **35**, 2891 (1902).
186. Jaffe, M. *Z. physiol. Chem.* **43**, 374 (1905).
187. Jaffe, M., and Hilbert, P. *Z. physiol. Chem.* **12**, 295 (1887–1888).
188. Jarrige, P. *Bull. soc. chim. biol.* **29**, 461 (1947).
189. Jensen, R., Snellman, O., and Sylvén, B. *J. Biol. Chem.* **174**, 265 (1948).
190. Jorpes, J. E. Heparin in the Treatment of Thrombosis: An Account of Its Chemistry, Physiology and Application in Medicine. 2nd ed., Oxford University Press, 1946.
191. Jorpes, J. E., and Bergström, S. *Biochem. J.* **33**, 47 (1939).
192. Julianelle, L. A. *J. Exptl. Med.* **44**, 113 (1926).
193. Kabat, E. A. *J. Biol. Chem.* **130**, 143 (1939).
194. Kapp, E. M., and Coburn, A. F. *J. Biol. Chem.* **145**, 549 (1942).
195. Karrer, P., Koenig, H., and Usteri, E. *Helv. Chim. Acta* **26**, 1296 (1943).
196. Karunairatnam, M. C., Kerr, L. M. H., and Levvy, G. A. *Biochem J.* **45**, 496 (1949).
197. Karunairatnam, M. C., and Levvy, G. A. *Biochem. J.* **44**, 599 (1949).
198. Katsuyama, K., and Hata, S. *Ber.* **31**, 2583 (1898).
199. Kendall, F. E., Heidelberger, M., and Dawson, M. H. *J. Biol. Chem.* **118**, 61 (1937).
200. Kertesz, Z. I. *J. Biol. Chem.* **108**, 127 (1935).
201. Kerr, L. M. H., Campbell, J. G., and Levvy, G. A. *Biochem. J.* **44**, 487 (1949).
202. Kim, M. S., and Ivy, A. C. *Proc. Soc. Exptl. Biol. Med.* **29**, 686 (1932).
203. Kleine, F. K. *Z. physiol. Chem.* **22**, 327 (1896–1897).
204. Kobert, R. *Z. klin. Med.* **62**, 1 (1907); *Chem. Zentr.* **1907**, I, 1804.

205. Kohl, M. F. F., and Flynn, L. M.   *Proc. Soc. Exptl. Biol. Med.* **47**, 470 (1941).

206. Kossel, A.   *Z. physiol. Chem.* **4**, 296 (1879–1880).

207. Kossel, A.   *Z. physiol. Chem.* **7**, 292 (1882–1883).

208. Kostanecki, St. V.   *Ber.* **19**, 2918 (1886).

209. Kuhling, O.   Inaug. Diss. Berlin (1887); cited by Williams (447).

210. Kuhn, R., and Löw, I.   *Z. physiol. Chem.* **254**, 139 (1938).

211. Külz, E.   *Arch. ges. Physiol. (Pflüger's)* **28**, 506 (1882).

212. Külz, E.   *Arch. ges. Physiol. (Pflüger's)* **30**, 484 (1883).

213. Külz, E.   *Z. Biol.* **27**, 247 (1890).

214. Lawrow, D.   *Z. physiol. Chem.* **32**, 111 (1901).

215. Lefevre, K. U., and Tollens, B.   *Ber.* **40**, 4513 (1907).

216. Lehmann, G., and Knoefel, P. K.   *Am. J. Med. Sci.* **197**, 639 (1939).

217. Lehmann, K. B.   *Arch. Hyg.* **72**, 307 (1910).

218. Lehmann, V.   *Z. physiol. Chem.* **13**, 181 (1888–1889).

219. Lesnik, M.   *Arch. exptl. Path. Pharmakol.* **24**, 167 (1887).

220. Lesnik, M., and Nencki, M.   *Ber.* **19**, 1534 (1886).

221. Levene, P. A.   Hexosamines and Mucoproteins.   Longmans, Green, London, 1925.

222. Levene, P. A.   *J. Biol. Chem.* **140**, 267 (1941).

223. Levvy, G. A.   *Biochem. J.* **40**, 396 (1946).

224. Lipschitz, W. L., and Bueding, E.   *J. Biol. Chem.* **129**, 333 (1939).

225. Loewi, O.   *Arch. exptl. Path. Pharmakol.* **47**, 56 (1901).

226. Machida, S.   *J. Chem. Soc. Japan* **64**, 1205 (1943).

227. Magnus-Levy, A.   *Biochem. Z.* **2**, 319 (1906).

228. Magnus-Levy, A.   *Biochem. Z.* **6**, 502 (1907).

229. Mahnert, F.   *Deut. med. Wochschr.* **14**, 1027 (1888).

230. Maisin, J., Pourbaix, Y., and Van de Voorde, C.   *Compt. rend. soc. biol.* **132**, 86 (1939).

231. Mandel, J. A., and Jackson, H. C.   *Am. J. Physiol.* **8**, xiii (1903).

232. Mandel, J. A., and Neuberg, C.   *Biochem. Z.* **13**, 148 (1908).

233. Mann, F., and Tollens, B.   *Ann.* **290**, 155 (1896).

234. Manville, I. A.   *Science* **85**, 44 (1937).

235. Maraldi, G.   *Boll. chim. farm.* **42**, 81 (1903).

236. Marrack, J., and Carpenter, B. R.   *Brit. J. Exptl. Path.* **19**, 53 (1938).

237. Marrian, G. F.   *Cold Spring Harbor Symposia Quant. Biol.* **5**, 16 (1937).

238. Marrian, G. F., and Gough, N.   *Biochem. J.* **40**, 376 (1946).

239. Marshall, E. K., Cutting, W. C., and Emerson, K.   *J. Am. Med. Assoc.* **110**, 252 (1938).

240. Martin, G. J., Fisher, C. V., and Thompson, M. R.   *Arch. Internal Med.* **69**, 662 (1942).

241. Martin, G. J., and Rennebaum, E. H.   *J. Biol. Chem.* **151**, 417 (1943).

242. Martin, G. J., Rennebaum, E. H., and Thompson, M. R.   *J. Biol. Chem.* **139**, 871 (1941).

243. Martin, G. J., Rennebaum, E. H., and Thompson, M. R.   *Ann. Internal Med.* **18**, 57 (1943).

244. Martin, G. J., and Thompson, M. R.   Brit. Patent 564,154, Sept. 15, 1944.

245. Martin, G. J., and Thompson, M. R.   U. S. Patent 2,366,742, Jan. 9, 1945.

246. Martin, G. J., Thompson, M. R., and Accousti, N. J.   *Am. J. Hyg.* **34D**, 23 (1941).

247. Masamune, H. *J. Biochem. Japan,* **19,** 353 (1934).

248. Mason, H. L., and Kepler, E. J. *J. Biol. Chem.* **161,** 235 (1945).

249. Mason, H. L., and Strickler, H. S. *J. Biol. Chem.* **171,** 543 (1947).

250. Maughan, G. B., Evelyn, K. A., and Browne, J. S. L. *J. Biol. Chem.* **126,** 567 (1938).

251. Mayer, P. *Z. klin. Med.* **47,** 68 (1902).

252. Mazur, A., and Shorr, E. *J. Biol. Chem.* **144,** 283 (1942).

253. McClean, D. *Biochem. J.* **37,** 169 (1943).

254. McClean, D., and Hale, C. W. *Biochem. J.* **35,** 159 (1941).

255. McCready, R. M., Swenson, H. A., and Maclay, W. D. *Ind. Eng. Chem., Anal. Ed.* **18,** 290 (1946).

256. v. Mering, J. *Z. physiol. Chem.* **6,** 480 (1882).

257. v. Mering, J. *Jahresber. Tierchem.* **14,** 241 (1885).

258. v. Mering, J. and Musculus, O. *Ber.* **8,** 662 (1875).

259. Meyer, A., and Jeannin, J. *Bull. soc. chim. biol.* **13,** 542 (1931).

260. Meyer, A. *Z. Vitaminforsch.* **14,** 332 (1944); *Chem. Abstracts* **41,** 2797 (1947).

261. Meyer, E. *Z. physiol. Chem.* **46,** 497 (1906).

262. Meyer, K. *Cold Spring Harbor Symposia Quant. Biol.* **6,** 91 (1938).

263. Meyer, K. *Advances in Protein Chem.* **2,** 249 (1945).

264. Meyer, K. *Physiol. Revs.* **27,** 335 (1947).

265. Meyer, K., Bloch, H. S., and Chaffee, E. *Federation Proc.* **1,** 125 (1942).

266. Meyer, K., and Chaffee, E. *Am. J. Ophthalmol.* **23,** 1320 (1940).

267. Meyer, K., and Chaffee, E. *J. Biol. Chem.* **133,** 83 (1940).

268. Meyer, K., and Chaffee, E. *J. Biol. Chem.* **138,** 491 (1941).

269. Meyer, K., and Palmer, J. W. *J. Biol. Chem.* **107,** 629 (1934).

270. Meyer, K., and Palmer, J. W. *Am. J. Ophthalmol.* **19,** 859 (1936).

271. Meyer, K., and Palmer, J. W. *J. Biol. Chem.* **114,** 689 (1936).

272. Meyer, K., Palmer, J. W., and Smyth, E. M. *J. Biol. Chem.* **119,** 501 (1937).

273. Meyer, K., and Smyth, E. M. *J. Biol. Chem.* **119,** 507 (1937).

274. Meyer, K., Smyth, E. M., and Dawson, M. H. *J. Biol. Chem.* **128,** 319 (1939).

275. Meyer, K., Smyth, E. M., and Palmer, J. W. *J. Biol. Chem.* **119,** 73 (1937).

276. Meyer, K. H., Odier, M. E., and Siegrist, A. E. *Helv. Chim. Acta* **31,** 1400 (1948).

277. Miller, C. O., Brazda, F. G., and Elliot, E. C. *Proc. Soc. Exptl. Biol. Med.* **30,** 633 (1933).

278. Miller, C. O., and Conner, J. A. *Proc. Soc. Exptl. Biol. Med.* **30,** 630 (1933).

279. Mills, G. T. *Biochem. J.* **43,** 125 (1948).

280. Mills, G. T., and Paul, J. *Biochem. J.* **44,** xxiv (1949).

281. Miriam, S. R., Wolf, J. T., and Sherwin, C. P. *J. Biol. Chem.* **71,** 249 (1927).

282. Mitsuba, K., and Ichihara, K. *Z. physiol. Chem.* **164,** 244 (1927).

283. Miura, S. *Biochem. Z.* **36,** 25 (1911).

284. Mörner, C. T. *Skand. Arch. Physiol.* **1,** 210 (1889).

285. Mörner, K. A. H. *Z. physiol. Chem.* **13,** 12 (1888–1889).

286. Mozolowski, W. *Biochem. J.* **34,** 823 (1940).

287. Müller, F. *Deut. med. Wochschr.* **13,** 27 (1887).

288. Müller, F. *Therap. Monatsh.* **2,** 355 (1888).

289. Mukerji, B., and Ghose, R. *Indian J. Med. Research* **27,** 765 (1940).

290. Munk, I. *Arch. ges. Physiol. (Pflüger's)* **12,** 142 (1876).

291. Myers, P. B., and Baker, G. L. *Delaware Agr. Expt. Sta. Bull.* **187** (1934).

292. Nakano, M. *Okayama-Igakkai-Zasshi* **44**, 1577 (1932); cited in *Japan. J. Med. Sci., II, Biochem.* **3**, (77) (1937).
293. Nasarijanz, B. A. *Schweiz. med. Wochschr.* **64**, 1090 (1934).
294. Neish, W. J. P. *Biochem. J.* **43**, 533 (1948).
295. Nencki, M. *Arch. Anat. Physiol.* **1870**, 399.
296. Nencki, M. *J. prakt. Chem. N. S.* **18**, 288 (1878).
297. Nencki, M. *Ber.* **27**, 2732 (1894).
298. Nencki, M., and Sieber, N. *Arch. ges. Physiol. (Pflüger's)* **31**, 319 (1883).
299. Neubauer, O. *Arch. exptl. Path. Pharmakol.* **46**, 133 (1901).
300. Neuberg, C. *Ber.* **33**, 3315 (1900).
301. Neuberg, C. *Biochem. Z.* **24**, 436 (1910).
302. Neuberg, C. *Berlin. klin. Wochschr.* **48**, 798 (1911).
303. Neuberg, C., and Gottschalk, A. *Biochem. Z.* **162**, 484 (1925).
304. Neuberg, C., and Kobel, M. *Biochem. Z.* **243**, 435 (1931).
305. Neuberg, C., and Kretschmer, E. *Biochem. Z.* **36**, 15 (1911).
306. Neuberg, C., and Niemann, W. *Z. physiol. Chem.* **44**, 114 (1905).
307. Neuberg, C., and Saneyoshi, S. *Biochem. Z.* **36**, 56 (1911).
308. Neuberg, C., and Schwenk, E. *Biochem. Z.* **79**, 383 (1917).
309. Newman, H. W., Van Winkle, W., Kennedy, N. K., and Morton, M. C. *J. Pharmacol.* **68**, 194 (1940).
310. Neymark, M. *Skand. Arch. Physiol.* **78**, 242 (1938).
311. Nishimura, K. *Japan. J. Med. Sci. IV, Pharmacol.* **8**, No. 3, *Proc. Japan. Pharmacol. Sci.* **9**, 111 (1935); *Chem. Abstracts* **30**, 3519 (1936).
312. Norman, A. G. *Nature* **143**, 284 (1939).
313. Norman, A. G., and Martin, J. T. *Biochem. J.* **24**, 649 (1930).
314. Novello, N. J., Harrow, B., and Sherwin, C. P. *J. Biol. Chem.* **67**, liv (1926).
315. Oberst, F. W. *J. Pharmacol.* **69**, 240 (1940).
316. Oberst, F. W. *J. Pharmacol.* **73**, 401 (1941).
317. Oberst, F. W. *J. Pharmacol.* **79**, 266 (1943).
318. Odell, L. D., Burt, J., and Bethea, R. *Science* **109**, 564 (1949).
319. O'Keeffe, A. E., Russo-Alesi, F. M., Dolliver, M. A., and Stiller, E. T. *J. Am. Chem. Soc.* **71**, 1517. (1949).
320. Oshima, G. *J. Biochem. Japan.* **20**, 361 (1934).
321. Oshima, Y. *J. Chosen Med. Assoc.* **21**, 562 (1931); *Chem. Abstracts* **26**, 3846 (1932).
322. Ottenberg, R., Wagreich, H., Berstein, A., and Harrow, B. *Arch. Biochem.* **2**, 63 (1943).
323. Owen, L. N., Peat, S., and Jones, W. J. G. *J. Chem. Soc.* **1941**, 339.
324. Palladin, A. V., and Palladina, L. *Ukraïn Biokhem. Zhur.* **7**, No. 2, 19 (1935); *Chem. Abstracts* **30**, 5620 (1936).
325. Partridge, S. M. *Biochem. J.* **43**, 387 (1948).
326. Pearce, R. H., and Watson, E. M. *Can. J. Research* **27E**, 43 (1949).
327. Perlstein, D., Wright, H. E., Liebmann, A. J., and Dorrell, I. *Science* **101**, 562 (1945).
328. Peterman, E. A. *J. Lancet* **67**, 451 (1947).
329. Pirie, A. *Brit. J. Exptl. Path.* **23**, 277 (1942).
330. Pohl, J., and Rawicz, M. *Z. physiol. Chem.* **104**, 95 (1919).
331. Porteous, J. W., and Williams, R. T. *Biochem. J.* **44**, 46 (1949).
332. Preusse, C. *Z. physiol. Chem.* **5**, 57 (1881).

333. Pryde, J., and Williams, R. T.   *Biochem. J.* **27**, 1210 (1933).
334. Pryde, J., and Williams, R. T.   *Biochem. J.* **28**, 131 (1934).
335. Pryde, J., and Williams, R. T.   *Biochem. J.* **30**, 794 (1936).
336. Pryde, J., and Williams, R. T.   *Biochem. J.* **30**, 799 (1936).
337. Pulaski, E. J., and Connell, J. F., Jr.   *Bull. U. S. Med. Dept.* **9**, 265 (1949).
338. Pulaski, E. J., Connell, J. F., Jr., and Seeley, S. F., paper presented at 98th Annual Session, American Medical Assoc., Atlantic City, June 8, 1949.
339. Quick, A. J.   *J. Biol. Chem.* **61**, 679 (1924).
340. Quick, A. J.   *J. Biol. Chem.* **67**, 477 (1926).
341. Quick, A. J.   *J. Biol. Chem.* **69**, 549 (1926).
342. Quick, A. J.   *J. Biol. Chem.* **70**, 59 (1926).
343. Quick, A. J.   *J. Biol. Chem.* **70**, 397 (1926).
344. Quick, A. J.   *J. Biol. Chem.* **77**, 581 (1928).
345. Quick, A. J.   *J. Biol. Chem.* **80**, 515 (1928).
346. Quick, A. J.   *J. Biol. Chem.* **80**, 535 (1928).
347. Quick, A. J.   *J. Biol. Chem.* **92**, 65 (1931).
348. Quick, A. J.   *J. Biol. Chem.* **95**, 189 (1932).
349. Quick, A. J.   *J. Biol. Chem.* **96**, 73 (1932).
350. Quick, A. J.   *J. Biol. Chem.* **96**, 83 (1932).
351. Quick, A. J.   *J. Biol. Chem.* **97**, 403 (1932).
352. Quick, A. J.   *J. Biol. Chem.* **98**, 537 (1932).
353. Ragan, C.   *Proc. Soc. Exptl. Biol. Med.* **63**, 572 (1946).
354. Ragan, C., and Meyer, K.   *J. Clin. Investigation* **28**, 56 (1949).
355. Rangier, M., and de Traverse, P.   *Compt. rend.* **208**, 1345 (1939).
356. Ratish, H. D., and Bullowa, J. G. M.   *Arch. Biochem.* **2**, 381 (1943).
357. Record, B. R., and Stacey, M.   *J. Chem. Soc.* **1948**, 1561.
358. Reeves, R. E.   *J. Am. Chem. Soc.* **62**, 1616 (1940).
359. Reeves, R. E., and Goebel, W. F.   *J. Biol. Chem.* **139**, 511 (1941).
360. Reinartz, F., and Zanke, W.   *Ber.* **69B**, 2259 (1936).
361. Reinartz, F., Zanke, W., and Faust, K.   *Ber.* **67B**, 1536 (1934).
362. Reinartz, F., Zanke, W., Schaefers, O., and Faust, K.   *Ber.* **67B**, 548 (1934).
363. Rimini, E.   *Atti accad. Lincei Classe sci. fis. mat. nat.* **10** (**5**), 244 (1901).
364. Rimini, E.   *Gazz. chim. ital.* **39** (II) 186 (1909).
365. Robinson, H. E., Gray, R. E., Chesley, F. F., and Crandall, L. A.   *J. Nutrition* **17**, 227 (1939).
366. Röckemann, W.   *Arch. exptl. Path. Pharmakol.* **92**, 52 (1922).
367. Ropes, M. W., Robertson, W. v. B., Rossmeisl, E. C., Peabody, B., and Bauer, W.   *Acta Med. Scand.* **128**, Suppl. 196, 700 (1947).
368. Salkowski, E., and Neuberg, C.   *Biochem. Z.* **2**, 308 (1906).
369. Salt, H. B.   *Biochem. J.* **29**, 2705 (1935).
370. Sammons, H. G., Shelswell, J., and Williams, R. T.   *Biochem. J.* **35**, 557 (1941).
371. Sammons, H. G., and Williams, R. T.   *Biochem. J.* **35**, 1175 (1941).
372. Sammons, H. G., and Williams, R. T.   *Biochem. J.* **40**, 223 (1946).
373. Saneyoshi, S.   *Biochem. Z.* **36**, 22 (1911).
374. Sauer, J.   *Klin. Wochschr.* **9**, 2351 (1930).
375. Scheff, G.   *Biochem. Z.* **183**, 341 (1927).
376. Scheunemann, B.   *Arch. exptl. Path. Pharmakol.* **100**, 51 (1923).
377. Schluchterer, E., and Stacey, M.   *J. Chem. Soc.* **1945**, 776.

378. Schmid, F. *Compt. rend. soc. biol.* **123**, 223 (1936).

379. Schmid, W. *Ann.* **93**, 83 (1855).

380. Schmiedeberg, O. *Arch. exptl. Path. Pharmakol.* **8**, 1 (1877).

381. Schmiedeberg, O., and Meyer, H. *Z. physiol. Chem.* **3**, 422 (1879).

382. Schüller, J. *Z. Biol.* **56**, 274 (1911).

383. Schultzen, O., and Naunyn, B. *Arch. Anat. Physiol.* **1867**, 349.

384. Schulz, O. *Jahresber. Tierchem.* **22**, 77 (1892).

385. Scudi, J. V. *Science*, **91**, 486 (1940).

386. Scudi, J. V., Buhs, R. P., and Hood, D. B. *J. Biol. Chem.* **142**, 323 (1942).

387. Scudi, J. V., and Robinson, H. J. *Am. J. Med. Sci.* **201**, 711 (1941).

388. Seastone, C. V. *J. Exptl. Med.* **70**, 361 (1939).

389. Sera, Y. *Z. physiol. Chem.* **88**, 460 (1913).

390. Sera, Y. *Z. physiol. Chem.* **90**, 258 (1914).

391. Sera, Y. *Z. physiol. Chem.* **92**, 261 (1914).

392. Shapiro, E. *Nature* **142**, 1036 (1938).

393. Shigenobu, T. *Ber. ges. Physiol. exptl. Pharmakol.* **63**, 627 (1932); cited by Williams (447).

394. Sieberg, E. *Z. physiol. Chem.* **97**, 53 (1916).

395. Simpson, S. A., and Smith, A. E. W. *Biochem. J.* **42**, 258 (1948).

396. Simpson, S. A., and Smith, A. E. W. *Biochem. J.* **44**, 366 (1949).

397. Siplet, H., Komarov, S. A., and Shay, H. *J. Biol. Chem.* **176**, 545 (1948).

398. Smith, F. *J. Chem. Soc.* **1944**, 584.

399. Smith, J. N. *Biochem. J.* **45**, 638 (1949).

400. Smith, J. N., and Williams, R. T. *Biochem. J.* **42**, 538 (1948).

401. Smith, J. N., and Williams, R. T. *Biochem. J.* **44**, 239 (1949).

402. Smith, J. N., and Williams, R. T. *Biochem. J.* **44**, 242 (1949).

403. Smith, J. N., and Williams, R. T. *Biochem. J.* **44**, 250 (1949).

404. Smith, R. J., private communication.

405. Snapper, I., Saltzman, A., and Greenspan, E. *Am. J. Digestive Diseases* **13**, 341 (1946).

406. Snapper, I., and Saltzman, A. *Arch. Biochem.* **24**, 1 (1949).

407. Stacey, M. *J. Chem. Soc.* **1939**, 1529.

408. Stacey, M. *Chemistry & Industry* **1943**, 110.

409. Stacey, M. *Advances in Carbohydrate Chem.* **2**, 161 (1946).

410. Stroud, J. *Endocrinology* **1**, 201 (1939).

411. Sundvik, E. *Jahresber. Tierchem.* **16**, 76 (1886).

412. Sylvén, B., and Larsson, L. G. *Cancer Research* **8**, 449 (1948).

413. Takao, K. *Z. physiol. Chem.* **131**, 304 (1923).

414. Tamura, S. *Acta Schol. Med. Univ. Imp. Kioto IV* **6**, 449, 454, 459 (1924); *Chem. Abstracts* **19**, 2705 (1925).

415. Taylor, E. W., Fowler, W. F., Jr., McGee, P. A., and Kenyon, W. O. *J. Am. Chem. Soc.* **69**, 342 (1947).

416. Teppati, R. *Arch. intern. pharmacodynamie* **57**, 440 (1937).

417. Thierfelder, H. *Z. physiol. Chem.* **10**, 163 (1886).

418. Thierfelder, H., and Daiber, K. *Z. physiol. Chem.* **130**, 380 (1923).

419. Thierfelder, H., and v. Mering, J. *Z. physiol. Chem.* **9**, 511 (1885).

420. Thomas, J. O., De Eds, F., and Eddy, C. W. *J. Pharmacol.* **64**, 280 (1938).

421. Thomas, P. *Bull. soc. chim. biol.* **7**, 102 (1925).

422. Tollens, B.   *Ber.* **41,** 1788 (1908).
423. Tollens, B., and Rorive, F.   *Ber.* **41,** 1783 (1908).
424. Tollens, C.   *Z. physiol. Chem.* **61,** 95 (1909).
425. Tracey, M. V.   *Biochem. J.* **43,** 185 (1948).
426. Vaubel, E.   *J. Exptl. Med.* **58,** 85 (1933).
427. Venning, E. M., and Browne, J. S. L.   *Proc. Soc. Exptl. Biol. Med.* **34,** 792 (1936).
428. Vescia, A.   *Boll. soc. ital. biol. sper.* **20,** 752 (1945); *Chem. Abstracts* **40,** 6628 (1946).
429. Vitali, D.   *Boll. chim. farm.* **38,** 377 (1899).
430. Voss, W., and Pfirschke, J.   *Ber.* **70B,** 631 (1937).
431. Watson, E. M., and Pearce, R. H.   *Am. J. Clin. Path.* **17,** 507 (1947).
432. Weber, C. J., Lalich, J. J., and Major, R. H.   *Proc. Soc. Exptl. Biol. Med.* **53,** 190 (1943).
433. Weber, H., and Heidepriem, C.   *Zentr. Gewerbehyg. Unfallverhüt.* **15,** 269 (1928).
434. Weigert, F.   *Nature* **155,** 479 (1945).
435. Weinmann, F.   *Ber.* **62B,** 1637 (1929).
436. Werch, S. C., and Ivy, A. C.   *Proc. Soc. Exptl. Biol. Med.* **48,** 9 (1941).
437. Whistler, R. L., Martin, A. R., and Harris, M.   *J. Research Natl. Bur. Standards* **24,** 13 (1940).
438. Wiley, F. H.   *J. Biol. Chem.* **124,** 627 (1938).
439. Williams, R. T.   *Biochem. J.* **32,** 878 (1938).
440. Williams, R. T.   *Biochem. J.* **32,** 1849 (1938).
441. Williams, R. T.   *Biochem. J.* **33,** 1519 (1939).
442. Williams, R. T.   *Biochem. J.* **34,** 48 (1940).
443. Williams, R. T.   *Biochem. J.* **34,** 272 (1940).
444. Williams, R. T.   *Biochem. J.* **34,** 690 (1940).
445. Williams, R. T.   *Biochem. J.* **37,** 329 (1943).
446. Williams, R. T.   *Biochem. J.* **40,** 219 (1946).
447. Williams, R. T.   Detoxication Mechanisms.   Wiley, New York, 1947.
448. Wise, L. E., and McCammon, D. C.   *J. Assoc. Official Agr. Chem.* **28,** 167 (1945).
449. Wolfrom, M. L., and Rice, F. A. H.   *J. Am. Chem. Soc.* **68,** 532 (1946).
450. Wolfrom, M. L., and Rice, F. A. H.   *J. Am. Chem. Soc.* **69,** 1833 (1947).
451. Wolfrom, M. L., and Rice, F. A. H.   *J. Am. Chem. Soc.* **69,** 2918 (1947).
452. Wolfrom, M. L., Weisblat, D. I., Karabinos, J. V., McNeely, W. H., and McLean, J.   *J. Am. Chem. Soc.* **65,** 2077 (1943).
453. Wright, S. E.   *Univ. Queensland Papers, Dept. Chem.* **1,** No. 25 (1945); cited by Williams (447).
454. Zondek, B.   *J. Urol.* **48,** 747 (1942).
455. Zondek, B.   *Nature* **149,** 334 (1942).
456. Zondek, B., and Shapiro, B.   *Biochem. J.* **37,** 592 (1943).

Index